Towards a Third Culture

TOWARDS A
THIRD CULTURE

by

CHARLES DAVY

FABER AND FABER

24 Russell Square

London

First published in mcmlxi
by Faber and Faber Limited
24 Russell Square, London, W.C.1
Printed in Great Britain by
Western Printing Services Ltd., Bristol

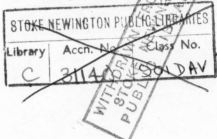

© *Charles Davy* 1961

To

those who have helped me

with this book, especially

A.B., O.A.B., G.A., O.W., J.C.D.,

and my wife

Contents

I. CONFUSION OF TONGUES *page* 11
II. FROM NEAR TO FAR 17
III. SEARCH FOR ANCESTORS 30
IV. NATURE DISPLAYED 40

★

V. THE FOCUS OF CONSCIOUSNESS 44
VI. BY ANY OTHER NAME 54
VII. EVERY MAN AN ISLAND 58
VIII. FIGURES OF ROMANCE 62
IX. DIVERGING STREAMS 71
X. THE ALCHEMISTS 76

★

XI. LOOK TO THE EARTH 81
XII. MODELS IN THE MIND 89
XIII. 'MAGICAL FEELING' 94

★

XIV. DANGEROUS KNOWLEDGE 104
XV. BEYOND THE MAP 111
XVI. NATURE'S LANGUAGE 119
XVII. THE GEOMETRY OF LIFE 128

★

XVIII. QUIET IN THE HEAD 134
XIX. FREEDOM AND FRATERNITY 142
XX. SEVEN YEARS 147

CONTENTS

XXI. RISE AND FALL *page* 155

XXII. RIVERS OF TIME 160

*

INDEX 175

CHAPTER I

Confusion of Tongues

In the spring of 1959 a brief phrase began an unexpected career. The occasion was the Rede Lecture given at Cambridge by Sir Charles Snow (C. P. Snow). He called it 'The Two Cultures and the Scientific Revolution'. Soon it was published as a pamphlet, and 'the two cultures' became the focus of a debate which ran for months through various journals, drew comments widely from abroad, and has still reached no conclusion.

Evidently, as Sir Charles said later,[1] he had touched a nerve—but not the nerve he had aimed at. The purpose of his lecture had been strictly practical; he had intended it as 'a call to action'. He had been impressed by two facts: the failure of education (especially in Britain and America) to take proper account of the twentieth-century scientific revolution, and the effects of this failure on the competition between Communism and the West to extend their influence by giving technical and capital aid to the poorer countries. If these countries were not given enough help by the West, they would get it from the Communists; and 'if that is how it turns out, we shall have failed both practically and morally. At best the West will have become an *enclave* in a different world—and this country will be the *enclave* of an *enclave*.'

But the subsequent debate was not much concerned with these questions. It fastened on Sir Charles Snow's picture of the two cultures and of the gap between them:

'I believe the intellectual life of the whole of western society is

[1] 'Afterthoughts', in *Encounter*, February 1960.

increasingly being split into two polar groups. . . . Literary intellectuals at one pole—at the other, scientists, and as the most
representative, the physical scientists. Between the two a gulf of
mutual incomprehension—sometimes (particularly among the
young) hostility and dislike, but most of all lack of understanding.
They have a curious distorted image of each other. Their attitudes
are so different that, even on the level of emotion, they can't find
much common ground.'

There were complaints that Snow had been less than fair to
some aspects of the old culture and more than fair to the new
culture, but hardly anyone denied that the gap existed, was harmful and ought to be closed. Snow himself had urged the need for
less early specialization in the schools, and on this familiar point
there was general agreement in principle; perhaps something will
even be done. But as a remedy, as a means of closing or bridg-
ing the gap, is it enough—is it nearly enough?

I began writing this book because it seemed to me that wider,
older issues are involved. The conflict between the two cultures
has not broken out suddenly today, nor does it exist only between
social groups. It is a conflict present also in many individuals,
something they can experience for themselves, and a not infre-
quent source of neuroticism and incapacity.

In its nineteenth-century form the conflict was usually a relatively straight and simple one between religion and science, often
resulting in a 'loss of faith'. The phrase sounds old-fashioned,
for the kind of literalist faith that used to be most readily shaken
by science is now rare, and today the issues are subtler and more
complicated. Religion and science have both taken up positions
in which the conflict between them is much less obvious and is
indeed often said to exist no longer: each has its separate province,
so why should they clash? Nevertheless, there is still a deep-
rooted conflict between the religious and the scientific pictures of
the universe; we will come to this later.

Moreover, the conflict can occur in individuals without religion
in any doctrinal form being involved. There can still be a painful
conflict between two outlooks: on one side, most of the values,
the experiences and apprehensions which seem to give meaning

to the world and to human living; on the other, all the facts—
all the hard, reliable facts: which may seem like saying, all the
truth.

If a young man (or equally a young woman) has been brought
up and educated in the old culture, if he responds to literature
and the arts and is not totally indifferent to religion, then, if he
begins to read and think about science, he may find it exciting—
and yet something in it may at the same time strike him like a
breath of cold air. He is liable to feel that if what science says
about the universe and the place of man within it is true and all
the truth, then literature and the arts, and even religion, can
hardly be more than temporary consolations and recreations, perhaps no more than a deceptively agreeable layer plastered over
the harsh foundations of the world. Without being false to his
own experience he cannot altogether accept this view of them;
but neither can he reject the chilling verdicts of science. What is
truth? It seems to be something he must swallow but cannot
digest. He feels as though the springs of his living were numbed,
frost-bound.

A young scientist is much less likely to come to this pass. He
is on a rising, not a waning, wave; and science may seem to give
him all he needs. For modern science can offer not only the
adventure of knowledge and the pride of power; it can bring
aesthetic satisfactions of a high order, and it may serve as a kind
of religion, providing an abundant sense of purpose and an
absorption in non-personal goals. Hence a young scientist may
feel (at least while he is fairly young and death is very far off)
that he can take anything he wants from the old culture without
taking it seriously—or not seriously enough to provoke any conflict between its values and his own.

But there are of course many scientists to whom the old culture
appeals more strongly than that; they are drawn to one or other
aspect of it because they feel in themselves some need which it
meets; or—more vaguely—because their own culture seems
somehow to be failing to give them all the nourishment they want.
They can avoid a conflict by keeping these two parts of their lives
in separate compartments, as is often done; but a potential conflict

between two sets of values and beliefs remains; the gap between the two cultures is not bridged.

It would of course be absurd to suggest that an awareness of the conflict is universal; millions of people are never exposed to it and have never heard of it; and, among those who are exposed to it, many on both sides manage to live fairly happily on their own side, or somewhere in the middle. If the conflict resulted merely in some individual tensions and distresses, it might hardly call for public concern, nor would Sir Charles Snow's lecture have led to so impassioned and protracted a debate.

He himself deplores the conflict for two reasons. First, because 'at the heart of thought and creation we are letting some of our best chances go by default. The clashing point of two subjects, two disciplines, two cultures—of two galaxies, so far as that goes —ought to produce creative chances. In the history of mental activity that has been where some of the breakthroughs came. The chances are there now. But they are there, as it were, in a vacuum, because those in the two cultures can't talk to each other.'

Secondly—and this for him is the immediately urgent and practical reason—because 'it is the traditional culture, to an extent remarkably little diminished by the emergence of the scientific one, which manages the western world', and because the consequences of this are those already mentioned: the western countries are failing to bring either their educational system or their world outlook into line with the demands and opportunities of the scientific revolution,[1] and are therefore likely to lose the

---

[1] 'By the industrial revolution,' Sir Charles says, 'I mean the gradual use of machines . . . the change in this country from a population mainly of agricultural labourers to a population mainly engaged in making things in factories and distributing them when they were made. . . . One can date it roughly from the middle of the eighteenth century to the early twentieth. Out of it grew another change, closely related to the first, but far more deeply scientific, far quicker, and probably far more prodigious in its result. This change comes from the application of real science to industry, no longer hit and miss, no longer the ideas of odd "inventors", but the real stuff . . . I believe the industrial society of electronics, atomic energy, automation, is in cardinal respects different in kind from any that has gone before, and will change the world much more. It is this transformation that, in my view, is entitled to the name of "scientific revolution".'

race with Communism for world leadership. Or—to put it in a less political and more human way—there are the hungry to be fed, the desperately poor to be lifted out of gross poverty; only science and technology can do it, and they are not being given the resources or the scope for the job.

These considerations are certainly enough to justify discussion of the two cultures and of the conflict between them; but I believe that still other issues are involved.

It seems certain that the new culture will continue to gain strength and influence, in company with the advance of science. In time the new culture (with an education corresponding to it) might become so dominant that the outlook and values of the old culture would survive only as eccentricities, and there would no longer be any gap left to bridge. This is not likely to happen during our generation in the West; but it has already happened to a great extent in Russia, and something like it seems to be happening with surprising speed in China. Hence, if we are ever going to bridge the gap, we ought not to delay.

This prospect of the dominance of an essentially scientific culture (even though in the West, if it were freed from Marxist dogma, it might be fairly liberal and humane) is one that Sir Charles Snow would certainly not welcome. He pays a warm tribute to the existing scientific culture, as manifest among the scientists he knows—'their culture is in many ways an exacting and admirable one . . . they are by and large the soundest group of intellectuals we have; there is a moral component right in the grain of science itself'—and he blames the literary intellectuals for assuming that theirs is the only real culture, 'as though the scientific edifice of the physical world was not, in its intellectual depth, complexity and articulation, the most beautiful and wonderful collective work of the mind of man'. But he also recognizes that scientists who regard the whole literature of the traditional culture as irrelevant in their interests are 'dead wrong. . . . Their imaginative understanding is less than it could be. They are self-impoverished.'

Hence he probably looks forward (though he doesn't enlarge

15

on this) to a unified culture, with the gap closed rather than bridged. But even if he is only hoping and calling for an effective bridge, the building of it may be more difficult than either he or other contributors to the debate seem to expect. Improvements in education, less specialization, endeavours to teach arts men some science and to give science students some acquaintance with literature and the arts—reforms of this kind could certainly do something. They could ease communication across the gap; but there would still be two outlooks, two languages.

In any event, the situation will not remain static; the present uneasy relation between the two cultures will not persist for ever unchanged; and whatever the change is, it will have considerable consequences for our ways of thinking and for the kind of world we make. Hence the questions I want to get on to are, roughly—where have the two cultures come from, why have they diverged, where are they going? We need to understand more about all this if we are to have any control over the direction of change. And I believe that in order to understand the history and prospects of the two cultures, we must relate them to a possibly unfamiliar subject, the evolution of consciousness.

But first I want to say a little more about the present divergence and to ask whether the existing scientific culture may not be in some respects less scientific, less in accord with the scientific method, than is perhaps usually recognized.

CHAPTER II

From Near to Far

The two cultures will not be brought together simply by improving communications between them: the difficulties are greater than that. Many modern scientists find it hard to enter into the spirit of the old culture and to feel at home there: its religious background seems to them to be bound up with outdated myths and superstitions, and it often appears to use pre-scientific ways of deciding what is useful and what is true. On the other side, anyone steeped in the old culture is likely to find the scientific picture of the world arid and disheartening.

This second point may not seem obvious, for superficially the new culture is—as Sir Charles Snow insists—optimistic. It has unbounded faith (which may be largely justified) in the power of modern science to give man a richer and healthier and longer life on earth, with a steadily increasing understanding of nature, including human nature, and command over it. In spite of the perils of nuclear war and the threat of over-population, it looks forward confidently to a future which will make the twentieth century seem a dark age. And yet—what will it all come to in the end? The final forecast is that the earth will be destroyed—perhaps burnt up by an expanding sun; and that man and all his works will be as though they had never been. Even if he succeeds in colonizing other planets, presumably outside the inhospitable solar system, the same ultimate fate will apply to them. Perhaps thousands or millions of years of scientific progress should be enough; but it is not an entirely satisfying prospect if in the end it all proves to be not only transient but humanly meaningless.

The scientific culture seems to carry silently within it, like a scarcely visible worm, this final negation of itself.

The *New Statesman* reviewer ('W.A.') of Sir Charles Snow's lecture asked, without answering, the question: 'Why has liberal humanism, which is based on a scientific view of man and the universe, failed on the whole to produce a body of literature adequate to it?'[1] Perhaps the short answer is that this scientific view of man and the universe fails to appeal to the unconscious; and unless the unconscious co-operates, good literature is never produced. One might explain this by saying simply that the unconscious, well known to be primitive and childish, is a long way yet from catching up with science. I would be inclined to add —yes, but there is also often evidence of a kind of wisdom in the unconscious, and perhaps it rebels against the scientific view of man and the universe because somehow it knows that this view is a long way from the truth. At any rate this is the first question I want to raise—if we respect and respond to modern science, how far must we accept the current scientific world-picture (*Weltanschauung*—we have no good word for it)?

Of course, if the scientific picture of the world and its ultimate fate had been finally established, we should have to make the best of it. But science cannot *prove* anything about the origin or final state of our planet; or about the character of the universe, aimless or purposeful; or whether any part of man survives death. These are not scientific questions; the attitude of science towards them should be agnostic, not committed to any confident opinion.

Many scientists, perhaps most, would agree with this; they would say that this is indeed their attitude; they see no reason for a conflict between science and religion unless religion clings to doctrines which fly in the face of scientific evidence, or claims to have infallible knowledge about matters which cannot be tested by any scientific means.

Nevertheless, the dominating influence of science on modern life has the effect of giving great prestige to an outlook which, although not properly part of science, is in the public mind

[1] *The New Statesman*, 6 June 1959.

inseparably associated with it, and is in fact given an almost dog-matic expression by some scientists—those who feel strongly that religion and most of the other attitudes bound up with the old culture are fetters on human progress.

Such utterances are unfair to science, in much the same way that fundamentalist utterances are unfair to religion—but they are made and they carry influence. Hence (in spite of soothing assurances to the contrary, whether from bishops or from mem-bers of the Royal Society) a fundamental conflict continues be-tween religion and science—or between religion and the 'liberal humanism' which claims to approach these questions in a scienti-fic way.

To say this does not imply a reactionary, 'anti-science' atti-tude—the attitude of those who dislike modern science and look back nostalgically to a time when life was simpler and happier, not bedevilled with all these dangerous modern inventions (but with all sorts of hideous pains and squalors which science has largely overcome). It implies only a wish that science should not disavow its own professed agnosticism by lending its authority to a world-picture which cannot be established by experimental proof. Science does often say 'I don't know', but perhaps not quite often or clearly enough.

One reason why the authority of science is so potent today is, of course, because of its prodigious practical achievements. Since it has obviously got hold of the right keys to so many doors, the ordinary man is inclined to suppose that it must be right also in its wider interpretations. But that is not the only reason. The scientific world-picture is readily accepted also because ordinary experience gives no obvious ground for questioning it. In other words, it faithfully reflects the mode of consciousness which prevails in our epoch. It *is* questioned, certainly, by reli-gious thinkers and by some other voices from the old culture, but generally on grounds of tradition and doctrine; and these sup-ports are tending all the time to weaken, while the prestige of science grows.

However, to discuss here the relation of the scientific outlook to modes of consciousness would anticipate later chapters. I want first to say something more about the range of reliable scientific knowledge and where it shades off into hypothesis and speculation. Many people, I believe, fail to appreciate the extent to which science makes use of extrapolations from the near and the known to the far and the unobservable. Because certain laws are found to hold good here and now, on the earth today, science generally assumes that they hold good everywhere and have held good ever since time (if it ever did begin) began.

These extrapolations are usually justified on the ground of the 'uniformity of nature', but this is itself no more than a hypothesis, plausible and convenient but unprovable. There is for example no proof, no certainty—however high the probability of it may seem to be—that the laws of earthly physics prevail unaltered throughout the reaches of astronomical space. We learn about the cosmos through phenomena produced in our instruments by signals which have to enter the earth-sphere in order to be observable, and are then interpreted by our consciousness through the instruments of eye and brain, which respond directly to only a very small range of signals. Cosmology is thus made up largely of hypotheses: these are necessary as aids and stimulants to further research, but to infer from them anything at all fundamental about the character of the universe is hazardous.

Similarly, there can be no proof that geophysical processes— up-thrusting, erosion, sedimentation and the like—have always proceeded at the rates assigned to them by modern observations. Yet a great deal in the accepted account of the earth's history depends on the validity of these far-reaching extrapolations.

Again, the layman may be inclined to assume that science has explained, or 'knows all about', some process which it has only described. A simple example is the action of a magnet on iron filings—nobody knows exactly how this apparent 'action at a distance' operates—and another is radio transmission, which can be precisely described mathematically and controlled, but involves the physically strange theory of wave-motion in a non-existent medium. Again, I have known at least one intelligent man who thought that by tracing the nerve processes and pathways concerned with seeing, science had fully accounted for the experience of conscious sight.

It would of course be absurd to say that science should 'stick to the facts' and abstain from theorizing. Facts in themselves are more or less meaningless; they acquire meaning only when they are interpreted by the human mind. A scientific interpretation often involves a theory which sets out to answer provisionally some question suggested by the facts. A good theory will give rise to predictions that can be tested by experiment. If the theory is confirmed, it will take rank as an accredited conceptual tool, brought into relation as far as possible with neighbouring theories, and used as a guide and a stimulant in further research.

These procedures are essential for the progress of science, even when they lead to the framing of theories which cannot be put to an immediate, decisive test. There is nothing wrong with that; it is how the scientific imagination naturally works. It is with the *next* step that science may exceed its proper bounds. This happens when a theory becomes a doctrine, which then has to be protected against attack. Some scientists may protest that in science there are no doctrines, no vested interests, but nobody familiar with scientific controversies will agree. If it were so, science would be a quite inhuman activity.

Science is indeed (as Sir Charles Snow says) an exacting discipline: its respect for facts, its insistence on controlled experiments for testing hypotheses, its dislike of vague verbiage and muddled emotionalism, its fostering of a previously rare objectivity both towards nature and towards oneself—all this adds up to an austere morality of a kind somewhat new in the history of mankind. If all scientists always lived up to it, they would hardly be human, and in these inhumanly virtuous scientists the fire of creative imagination, often unruly, might sometimes be chilled. But with an austere morality there often go certain dangers: tendencies to pride, self-righteousness, dogmatism—they are well known. I think they are sometimes manifest in the scientific field: if, for instance, it is assumed that if anything appears to

happen contrary to an accepted law of nature, it *cannot* really have
happened; anyone who claims to have observed it is dishonest or
deceived.[1] Scientists are generally quite ready to investigate some
apparent anomaly in the functioning of a natural law, but as a
rule only if the phenomenon seems to call for a revision of the
law, not if it seems to be radically incompatible with it.

Some years ago a young Swiss writer, Robert Crottet, gave a
B.B.C. radio talk[2] about the Skolt Lapps, a simple, charming
people with whom he had lived for a long period in the Arctic
forests. He described, incidentally, how they appear to use some
kind of telepathy for getting news of each other: a man will know
if a friend at some distance has fallen ill or if a neighbour has set
out to visit him. Mr. Crottet told of occasions when this method
of communication seemed to work as reliably as a postal service.
He may have been deceived, but he gave the impression of being
a patient observer, not a crank.

If he had reported the discovery of a heap of buried bones
which seemed likely to yield new information about some long
extinct creature whose very existence, previously surmised from
a few fragments, had been in doubt, some scientists would probably have gone out fairly promptly to investigate. Mr. Crottet's
talk, as far as I know, roused no ripple of interest in scientific
circles. Yet it might have proved to be a pointer to a survival
equally rare, and (from a human point of view) much more
significant.

By now, a good deal of evidence favouring telepathy has
accumulated from card-guessing experiments, but it is not uni-
versally accepted, and in any event the Lapp telepathy, if it had
been verified, would have been more satisfying, less open to

---

[1] A minor example is that of highly diluted ('high potency') homoeopathic remedies. Their mode of action is unknown, but they have been
used for well over a century by many fully-qualified doctors in many
countries. Doctors who use them generally become convinced by clinical
experience that they do act on the human organism, and innumerable case-
histories are on record in homoeopathic journals and books. Hence it
seems rash to assume that because these remedies seem to make no chemical sense, any results they produce *must* be due to suggestion and nothing
more.

[2] An extract was printed in *The Listener*, 7 July 1948.

arguments about the validity in this connection of statistical probability.

Plenty of similar examples could be given from the history of psychical research and kindred subjects, but there is no need. It may be more profitable to ask *why* science is generally so reluctant to explore these borderland phenomena. I can think of four reasons, none of which seems quite to justify the reluctance, and of a fifth reason which—if it ever actually came into play— I would regard as the best of the lot.

Arthur Koestler describes in one of his autobiographical volumes how in 1952 he met at Princeton an old friend, the late Hans Reichenbach, a leading mathematical logician and Professor of Philosophy in the University of California:

'He had aged and become partly deaf; instead of a modern hearing-aid, he used an old-fashioned ear-trumpet. He asked me what I had been interested in lately, and I told him that I had become interested in Rhine's work on extra-sensory perception. He said it was all hokum, and I said I did not think so—at least the statistical evaluation of the experiments seemed to show relevant results (meaning that they seemed to confirm the existence of telepathy and kindred phenomena). Reichenbach smiled and asked: "Who has checked the statistics?" I said: "R. A. Fisher in person." (Fisher is one of the leading contemporary experts in probability calculus.) Reichenbach adjusted his trumpet: "Who did you say?" I yelled into the trumpet: "Fisher, *the* Fisher." At that moment an extraordinary change took place in Reichenbach's face. He went pale, dropped his trumpet, and said: "If that is true, it is terrible, terrible. It would mean that I would have to scrap everything and start from the beginning." '[1]

Episodes with this somewhat melodramatic flavour are doubtless rare. But I think it is true that scientists are often reluctant to examine certain phenomena because, *if* they proved to be genuine, they would disturb too many prevailing scientific ideas.

That is the first reason; closely allied to it is a second. A scientist may fear that if he were known to be mixed up with any of these queer phenomena, his scientific reputation would suffer.

[1] *The Invisible Writing*, 1954.

One can hardly blame him, especially if he is a young man with his name still to make. But if science were quite free from unscientific 'establishment' tendencies, and always ready to follow the facts wherever they might lead, these fears would hardly arise.

A third reason is that the investigation of borderland phenomena often proves them to be spurious, if not fraudulent, or it leads to maddeningly inconclusive results, and scientists have little time to spare for such inquiries. Why should they turn aside from their regular work to study some apparently irrational occurrence which will probably turn out to have some simple or trivial explanation? But this kind of objection may often be a rationalization: it would never be advanced in connection with any orthodox branch of science. Think of the endless patience and perseverance devoted nowadays to all kinds of laboratory researches, even those not expected to yield more than a tiny grain of highly specialized information.

A fourth motive is much more respectable. It derives from a conviction that 'all this' belongs to a realm of superstitions from which mankind, aided by science, has at last begun to escape. To many scientists it feels like an escape from a murky, unhealthy twilight into the clear daylight of hard facts and rational thinking. And there must be no return, even if it means refusing to investigate plausible findings in this field. Far better that they should be ignored and quietly buried than that science should be infected, and encouragement given to a dangerous revival of pre-scientific ways of thought.

This attitude is understandable and to some extent justified: we will return to it when we consider the relation of modern science to earlier forms of knowledge. Here I will say only that I shall not be arguing in favour of 'going back' to anything, or of obstructing or limiting scientific advance. It has been essential for science to shake itself free from medievalism, and it remains essential for it to keep the edge of its own thinking clear and bright. What I shall argue is that there are no *scientific* grounds for dismissing as worthless all the older ways of thinking; and that in order to see the development of modern science in perspective, we must reckon with loss as well as gain.

There is something of a parallel, perhaps, in the stern attitude of the Christian Fathers towards the old pagan rites and gods. And to some extent they, too, were justified: it *would* have been dangerous for early Christianity to give free play to all the influences from Eastern mystery-religions, by then mostly decadent, which pervaded the Graeco-Roman world, or free rein to all its own heresies. But Christianity was seriously impoverished by the extreme zeal of the Fathers in cutting it off from earlier sources of wisdom and thus driving its esoteric stream (manifest up to the time of Origen at least) underground.[1] Modern science, too, may suffer if it regards as superstition almost all earlier claims to know anything reliable about the nature of the world and of man.

But this is not an easy question: I feel in two minds about some aspects of it. The phenomena reported from the borderlands cover a wide range: they include telepathy, clairvoyance, precognition, psychometry and crystal gazing, various forms of mediumship, apparitions, hauntings and poltergeists, levitation, dowsing and radiesthesia, deep hypnosis phenomena and 'astral travelling', and the rare occasions when a scene from the past appears to make itself visible or audible in the present.[2] Reading the more sober records in these fields (the literature is of course enormous, but a high proportion of it is valueless) gives me the impression that the ordinary world we perceive and deal with is like a fairly thin crust over regions where quite other possibilities prevail.

Something similar can be felt about the threshold between conscious and unconscious. Up above (to speak metaphorically) there is clear consciousness, self-possession, logic, objectivity, or at any rate the possibility of them; down below are dream-images, archetypes, obsessions, a crazy kind of logic governed by

[1] Something similar took place on a more limited scale when Celtic Christianity was vanquished at the Synod of Whitby, A.D. 664.

[2] The well-known Versailles case, 'An Adventure', has been widely disputed. A much more strongly attested and carefully checked example is the Dieppe Raid case. The battle-sounds of this 1942 operation were apparently heard in vivid detail for about two hours in the early morning by two English ladies who were on holiday at Puys, near Dieppe, in August 1951. See the *Journal* of the Society for Psychical Research, May–June 1952.

emotion, and a flux of psychic energies capable of unseating the mind if they get loose. Nor is this a quite arbitrary analogy, for actually to explore the borderlands—as distinct from reading about them—often involves some surrender of conscious control: it need not always do so but generally it does, if the inquirer is in any way using himself as an instrument. Moreover, the phenomena nearly always seem to depend on tapping unconscious psychic forces: telepathy is not a conscious process, and even such apparently physical phenomena as the antics of poltergeists seem to require the co-operation (not always consciously fraudulent) of a human being, generally an adolescent. One could almost say that to explore the borderlands *is* to explore the unconscious, and not only to explore it but to open it up, and that is always a dangerous procedure, as psychiatry well knows.

However, one must draw certain distinctions. There is a distinction between the subconscious and unconscious on the one hand and the superconscious on the other, a distinction not easy to define but important; and supernormal faculties *can* be acquired without loss of conscious control: we will come to this later. Again, the borderland phenomena are not all on the same footing. Those involving trance mediumship—whether used for 'communications' or for producing physical phenomena—are peculiarly liable to deception and fraud (it need not be conscious fraud on the medium's part).[1] The most dangerous types of phenomena may be those elicited through deep hypnosis and those associated with dowsing and radiesthesia.

The practical possibilities of hypnosis have often been over-

---

[1] An example of how unsure the ground is in this realm, even when no evident dishonesty occurs, is the Gordon Davis case. A man giving this name unexpectedly 'came through' a direct-voice medium (a woman) while the sitter was trying to contact his brother, killed in the First World War. The man not only gave the sitter, an old school friend, some accurate details about his past life but spoke with an intonation which the sitter immediately recognized as characteristic of Gordon Davis. Moreover, he plainly indicated that he was dead. It turned out that Gordon Davis was still alive; at the same time of the sitting he had been pursuing his normal business as a house-agent in Southend, in complete ignorance of his own apparent manifestation at the séance. See the *Proceedings* of the Society for Psychical Research, December 1925.

dramatized in popular fiction, but some hypnotic methods, combined perhaps with modern 'brain-washing' techniques, could yield dangerous powers of invading the personality of a suitable subject and manipulating any psychic gifts he or she might have.

Ordinary dowsing, or water-divining, seems harmless enough, although this use of some unconscious parts of the human organism as a detection instrument may not be entirely healthy in our epoch. But when similar methods are employed in connection with blood-spots for various medical purposes, as they are in radiesthesia, potential dangers, do, I believe, exist. Methods of working on the life-forces of the human organism—methods capable perhaps of healing but also of harming—might be developed in this largely uncharted field.

So long as the exploration of the borderlands remains on a kind of mainly amateur basis, any such dangers are not likely to become serious. But the situation might soon change if the professional resources of modern science were turned on the job, rather as they have been applied, for example, to exploring the subatomic world. Hence if scientists were to resolve to keep clear of some of the borderlands for *this* reason—because of the potential dangers involved—I would call it a good reason; but I have never heard this reason advanced.

This does not mean that in the amateur exploration of these realms—since this is bound to continue, whatever doubts or objections might be raised—scientific *methods* should not be employed. This is certainly desirable, if only as a safeguard against fraud and sheer waste of time. But I am not anxious to see the professionals take over the whole territory just yet.

The *attitude* of science towards the borderlands is a different question. A scientist might reasonably say: 'I don't want to be drawn into these fields: I think I can spend the time better on work more likely to yield reliable results. There do seem to be some queer phenomena which probably can't be explained at present in ordinary scientific terms. Why not? Modern science has been going for only about 300 years and there is bound to be a lot it hasn't touched. We try to find out how nature works: we don't suppose nowadays that we are discovering final truths. Very likely the universe is a great deal stranger than we generally suppose.'

This indeed may be the attitude of many scientists, more or less, but one seldom hears it explicitly expressed. When the more vocal scientists speak or write publicly about science, the impression often given is that there is a gradually extending area of scientific knowledge, a brightly lit area, and outside it nothing but rather dim regions haunted by popular fallacies and the ghosts of old beliefs. A further implication is that, although a great deal about the universe is not yet scientifically known, enough is known to establish with fair certainty what kind of universe it is that we inhabit. This is not a scientific conclusion, and I am not saying that many scientists do or would put it forward in exactly that form. I am speaking of the impression left on all the people, quite numerous today, who are interested enough to listen to what science says, but without considering exactly where proof ends and speculation begins.[1]

In this chapter I have been concerned more with the public face of science than with science itself. Purely scientific concepts seldom have much chance to become authoritarian; there may be a last-ditch resistance to some new finding, but before very long, if the finding is confirmed, the rules (and later on the textbooks) are revised. Modern physics has been through several revolutions in this century and there may be more to come. It is when scientists look out from their own stronghold towards other fields of belief or inquiry, present or past, that a doctrinal note, foreign to pure science but carrying the authority of science, is fairly often heard—sometimes even with echoes of the attitude attributed mythically to Dr. Jowett:

I am Master of this College,
What I know not is not knowledge.

[1] 'People fail to distinguish between a new theory about the origin of life (or the origin of granite or of petroleum), which is merely one more speculative idea, and a theory from which flow new consequences that can be tested. Speculation in the field of cosmogony is not to be disparaged, but the wide publicity given to each new flight of fancy tends to confuse the general public and encourage credulity.' James B. Conant, *Modern Science and Modern Man* (Bampton Lectures), 1952.

The effect is that many unproven opinions—both positive views and negative condemnations—gain wide currency in the name of science, and the minds of many people come to be imprisoned in a thought-system which they take to be much more final and authoritative than it really is—and much more authoritative than most working scientists would ever want or mean it to be.

The recurrent debates about evolution are an example: in this wide field the boundaries between facts and surmise are often not clearly drawn.

CHAPTER III

Search for Ancestors

There is overwhelming evidence that evolution has occurred, on Darwinian lines, and that natural selection, acting
on small genetic variations, has played a very great part
in it. Whether this is enough to account for the whole process,
including the emergence of the human consciousness which
critically surveys the process, is uncertain.

The prevailing scientific theory—Neo-Darwinism—cannot be
proved to be all-sufficient, nor can it be proved not to be, and
for much the same reason—lack of conclusive evidence. There
are too many gaps in the record, too many 'mays' and 'mights',
not enough for argument to get hold of. Hence a scientific approach, it seems to me, should quite explicitly treat the *sufficiency*
of the theory as an open question—open to new evidence, new
ideas and interpretations, not closed by dogmatism on any
side.

One day I watched (in the south of France) a dragon-fly
skimming over a pool. It had two pairs of wings and a brilliant
blue body. The two pairs of wings could no doubt have evolved
by very small stages, each conferring a certain advantage; perhaps also the blue body, though one might think it dangerously
conspicuous. But my instinctive feeling was—here is a miracle of
workmanship, a marvellous piece of mechanism. Yes, mechanism,
for the insect's behaviour could perhaps all be explained in terms
of tropisms and pre-set responses. But to attribute the whole
thing to natural selection acting on genetic variations seems to
me rather like supposing that a miniature watch, so finely wrought

as to be almost a work of art, could come about by similar means. The idea of the watch would have to be there first.

Or there are plenty of puzzles, of the type that lead people to exclaim, 'How can natural selection acting on random variations have brought about these extraordinary ways of life?' For example, the metamorphosis of insects, from caterpillar through amorphous pupa to an entirely different winged form. (An odd fact here is that in some cases the organs of the future butterfly are visibly imprinted on the *outside* of the pupa at an early stage, like a pattern of what is to come, although inside the pupa there is nothing but the old body of the larva, in process of breaking down.) Or the unexpected relations between certain sea-slugs and the poisonous coelenterates on which they feed. Or the familiar but still astonishing organization of a beehive, and the 'dance' whereby the bees back from foraging indicate very precisely the direction and distance of the food-supply.

However, the strongest impression I have on looking at nature is not connected with evolutionary puzzles but with something rather different—the wealth of forms which strike the human mind as having a quality of artistic design. The tiny tropical fish in an aquarium look to me like jeweller's work (and the sea-horse, shaped like a chessboard knight, looks like the work of a jeweller with a sense of humour). I am not forgetting the many aspects of nature which from a human point of view appear unpleasant, repulsive, even sinister: in these too there are some remarkable puzzles (the life-history of the liver-fluke, for example), but also many instances where the element of artistic design is prominent, even though it may be associated with activities inimical to human living. I find it hard to imagine that this extraordinary spectacle has arisen from mindless variations, worked on by mindless selective agencies. The end-product appears to have a character and quality altogether out of line with the supposed process. But this is an aesthetic judgment, and aesthetic judgments are always personal—no use arguing about them.

To return to the puzzles, many examples of them are admittedly beyond the range of detailed explanation, at present, but they do not prove anything. Or, rather, they do prove something

—that a far-reaching selective process has been at work. If puzzles of this kind are put to a Neo-Darwinist, he usually says: 'These remarkable adaptations have obviously not come about by pure chance—the odds against that are fabulous. We know that natural selection has been active in picking out and conserving favourable variations, and there is no evidence of any other agency directing the course of evolution. Therefore it is reasonable to regard these so-called puzzles as evidence *for* natural selection and its power, not as evidence against.'

R. A. Fisher, who uses this argument, says in the same article[1] that the puzzles 'are all, in somewhat different ways, difficulties less of the reason than of the imagination'. Or, as Julian Huxley puts it in the introductory chapter to this symposium, 'Selection, given sufficient time, is competent to produce adaptations of extreme delicacy and functional organs of extreme complexity: it is the limitations of our imaginative faculty which prevent us from realising this fact.'

This way of dealing with the 'puzzles' is perhaps not entirely convincing. 'Because we know of no other agency than natural selection, then natural selection must have done everything'—logically, this seems weak. And to say that we should understand how natural selection is capable of producing even the most apparently improbable and bizarre results if we had stronger imaginations—surely there is some begging of the question there. But it is fair enough for a Neo-Darwinian to say: 'This is the best theory we have. We don't claim that it explains everything, but it explains a very great deal, and it leads on fruitfully to genetical and biochemical research. If you can advance a better theory, backed with an equal amount of solid evidence, we will listen. Until then, we shall stick to our own. It is still a rapidly developing theory, much stronger now than it was even twenty years ago.'

This last point is important: critics of evolutionary theory do not always recognize how far its resources of explanation have

[1] 'Retrospect of Criticisms of Natural Selection', in the symposium, *Evolution as a Process*, edited by Julian Huxley, A. C. Hardy and E. B. Ford, 1954.

expanded recently, partly through advances in genetics. For example, selection is no longer supposed to act only on mutations, small or large, but also on the slight variations that arise within a species through 'genetical recombination'. In any animal population some members of the same species will be, let us say, a little larger than others, not because their genes are different but because their genes are combined in a way that makes for an above average body-size. Then, if conditions favour this extra size, they will be selected for survival at the expense of their smaller fellows. 'Genetical recombination' gives natural selection a much wider range of material to work on than could be expected from mutations alone.

Then there is 'adaptive radiation', whereby variations of a dominant species radiate out to fill all the available niches in a given environment. If the environment offers plenty of scope, and not much competition from rival species, a diversity of sub-species will arise. Here the environment is seen as exerting a more positive influence on evolution than it was formerly thought to do: *its* varieties may promote variety in its inhabitants.

The term 'adaptive radiation' is fairly new, but the process was in fact noted by Darwin when he landed on the Galapagos Islands during the voyage of the *Beagle*. He found that in this isolated environment a race of finches had branched out into a number of new families, with very diverse habits, while the parent stock on the mainland had remained virtually unchanged. It was this contrast which first strongly impressed the idea of evolution on his mind.[1]

A further recent development in the explanatory resources of Neo-Darwinism comes from close observation of animal behaviour. It has been found that surface features which to us seem to be ornamental, perhaps, but of no practical utility, may play an essential part, as 'releasers', in starting off certain necessary trains of action—concerned perhaps with the defence of territory or with the courtship-reproduction cycle—in another animal (or bird). Hence it is reasonable to suppose that such features, since

---

[1] See David Lack, *Darwin's Finches*, 1947.

33

they tend to make behaviour more efficient, have been gradually developed by natural selection.

Probably not all apparently useless features and adaptations can be interpreted in this way; for these, other explanations are available. First, a favourable genetic modification may be accompanied (through the interaction of genes) by some other minor modification with no positive survival value; both are then likely to be conserved. Secondly, in small populations differentiations may arise without the aid of selection, but through the chance fixation of some new mutation or recombination ('genetic drift').

Finally, there is a point which may seem too familiar to mention, but to keep hold of its full implications is not so easy. I mean the vast expanse of time over which natural selection is believed to have been at work. If one thinks what a century means in human terms, then tries to picture a thousand centuries, ten thousand . . . the mind soon falters. But ten thousand centuries are only one million years, and life is thought to have existed on earth for about 500 million years.

These vast time-scales are of course arrived at largely by extrapolating freely from certain assumptions, the main one being that physical processes—e.g. erosion, sedimentation, radio-active decay—have always gone on at about the same rate as they do now. This is a plausible assumption, with no clear evidence against it, but it *is* an assumption. It is also possible that calculations based on modern observations are valid only for a relatively modern phase in the earth's long history. However, anyone inclined to doubt whether natural selection can do all that is claimed for it should at least appreciate that the prevailing theory allows it enough time for doing almost anything. As Julian Huxley puts it:

'Thanks to the work of such men as R. A. Fisher, H. J. Muller, J. B. S. Haldane, and Sewall Wright, it is now clear that selective advantages, so small as to be undetectable in any one generation, are capable, when operating on the scale of geological time, of producing all the observed phenomena of biological evolution, such as the formation of new species, the adaptive radiation of groups into specialized sub-groups, the succession of dominant types, and even the most apparently improbable adaptations.'[1]

The work referred to is severely mathematical: it is not concerned with what *has* happened but with what *can* happen—is 'capable' of happening—in terms of statistical probability:

'Supposing there are no changes in the environment which would alter the force of selection while a character was spreading through a population, the mathematicians have been able to show that the character will spread if its selective advantage is not smaller than $1/N$ where N is the number of effectively breeding individuals in the population. In large populations, with more than 1,000 individuals, this advantage is very small, far smaller than we could hope to demonstrate by observation or experiment. In smaller populations the necessary advantage is larger and selection will be less effective.'[2]

In spite of all this, some questions and uncertainties remain. One question arises very early in the geological record. The oldest invertebrate fossils are of quite complicated creatures, suggesting long periods of evolutionary history already behind them.[3] The obvious assumption is that they were preceded by simpler forms which have vanished without trace (as could easily have happened, since the extant fossils from any period are rare survivals, preserved by exceptional conditions). But this seems obvious only because we take it for granted that evolution is always and necessarily from the simple to the complex. This appears to be the way of organic growth from seed to adult form, but even here it may not be the whole story; and I think there are evolutionary processes (as we shall see later in connection with the evolution of consciousness) which follow a different course—one of contraction rather than expansion; or one might call it a process whereby

---

[1] *Evolution as a Process*, op. cit., p. 3.

[2] G. S. Carter, *A Hundred Years of Evolution*, 1957, p. 140.

[3] 'Nearly all phyla which leave any kind of fossil record are well represented in Cambrian rocks—many of them by several groups, which already show the distinctive character of modern classes. Why pre-Cambrian fossils are so rare is not yet understood.' Ralph Buchsbaum, *Animals Without Backbones*, Vol. Two, p. 351 (Pelican, 1951).

simpler elements are led to separate out from a rich multiplicity (or sometimes from 'chaos', in the old sense of the word). The two processes are complementary: in the total picture of evolution we have to imagine them going on at the same time.

To return to Darwinian evolution and natural selection, a problem not fully solved is that 'in the genotypes of organisms, as we find them in nature, most of the genes are in the dominant condition. But most of the mutations that arise in nature are recessive. Does this mean that only the relatively rare dominant mutations (7 per cent in Drosophila) are used in evolution?'[1] Whether R. A. Fisher's theory of the 'evolution of dominance' goes all the way to the answer seems to be undecided.

The main problems, however, are concerned not with variations within a species (micro-evolution), but with the emergence of new species (macro-evolution). Variations within a species will mostly tend towards greater specialization: they will survive because they make an organism more efficiently adapted to a particular environment. But what happened at the times of the great transitions—when reptiles evolved from fishes or amphibians at the beginning of the Mesozoic era, or when the birds and mammals emerged at the beginning of the Tertiary? The earliest examples of a new species are relatively unspecialized: how can they have evolved from highly specialized ancestors?[2]

To put it in more general terms, selection leads to a wide variety of specialized forms: many die out and some persist. Those that survive do so because they are adapted to a particular niche in the prevailing environment. But the more successful they are, the less open are they to further variation, for any further variation would be likely to make them less nicely adjusted to the demands of their niche. How, then, can selection have favoured the emergence from them of a new, unspecialized type?

More briefly still, micro-evolution leads to specialized organisms in blind-alleys; macro-evolution calls for new starts.

Neo-Darwinism has a partial answer to this problem. A

[1] G. S. Carter, op. cit., p. 141.
[2] Cf. John Waterman, 'Evolution and the Image of Man', in *The Faithful Thinker* (Hodder and Stoughton, 1961).

Mexican aquatic lizard, the Axolotl, becomes sexually mature and breeds while the rest of its organism is relatively undeveloped. This phenomenon, *neotony*, is found also in a few other species, and there is evidence that it may have occurred on various occasions in the distant past—that the first vertebrates, for instance, arose not from adult invertebrates, but from invertebrates which had become able to breed in the plastic larval stage before developing into specialized adults:

'However highly specialised a race of animals may have become in its typical adult condition, provided it has a less or differently specialised young or larval form (which will naturally be well adapted to its particular mode of living), and has a gene-complex which may sooner or later produce neotony, then given time it stands a chance of escape from its path to extinction. In the great majority of stocks the end must come before this rare opportunity of paedomorphosis can intervene; but in a very small minority the chance comes earlier, before it is too late, and such lines are switched by selection to new pathways with fresh possibilities of adaptive radiation. So vast is the span of time available, that, rare as they may be, these escapes from specialisation seem likely to have provided some of the more fundamental innovations in the course of evolution.'[1]

The seemingly sad faces of apes are those of creatures which have diverged from the path that led to the most unspecialized of animals, man. But an infant ape is much more human-like than an adult; as it grows up it rapidly diverges and becomes more specialized. This may suggest that the bodily ancestors of the first men were simian creatures who were still plastic, not yet committed to specialized blind-alleys. But we do not know exactly how or when the first men appeared, and there is no evidence that neotony was responsible for it. Indeed, although it seems certain that specialization and its counter-process, retention or renewal of plasticity, are basic features of the evolution story, it appears unlikely on present showing that at every crisis in the story neotony came in to help things through.

[1] A. C. Hardy, F.R.S., 'Escape from Specialisation', contributed to *Evolution as a Process*, op. cit.

The story as a whole seems to me to suggest that natural selection has played a major part in determining the evolution of specialized variations on the main animal (and vegetable) prototypes, but that question-marks stand at the great transition points when new prototypes appear. And a rather different question-mark at the point when human beings emerge, for it is not easy to imagine how natural selection can account for the transition from animal to human consciousness, with its conceptual thinking, its command of language and its moral sense. At the other great transition-points it is as though a new archetypal idea comes to expression in a new type of organism; at this last transition-point it is more as though a new being takes form on the earth; a being able to raise itself erect, to shape its larynx for speech and its brain for thinking, free from the specialized degenerations now manifest in the apes.

There is no clear evidence for these ways of looking at evolution, nor is there firm evidence against them. They are not incompatible with the facts on which Neo-Darwinism is based, but only with some of the theories and opinions built up on the facts. If these opinions—e.g. that man *must* have evolved solely through natural selection, and that any other notion of his origin and nature is moonshine—are put forward as though they had the authority of science behind them, they have an imprisoning effect on minds. Yet it is only just over 100 years since *The Origin of Species* was first published: it would be surprising if already we knew just how all the extraordinary results of evolution have come about. They can hardly fail to arouse wonder in anyone who contemplates them, most of all perhaps in the scientists who know most about them. But if wonder is the beginning of philosophy, there is a sense in which it brings science to a stop. A practising scientist has to limit his indulgence in wonder, or instead of investigating he would simply stand and stare. He has to forgo contemplation in order to extend detailed knowledge, as when he dissects a flower or a frog.

It does not follow, however, that wonder is merely an emotional reaction, with no bearing on the character of the world. If we were not dulled by habit and routine we should feel it continually: we should go about in a state of perpetual wonder at the astonishing spectacle of the universe around us. The mere fact that such a universe exists at all is staggering enough. How did it all begin (if it ever did)? And how did we get here, in the midst of the universe, but sufficiently not part of it to be staggered by it?

Such questions tease us out of thought, but they are not quite frivolous. The impulse to ask them and the inability to answer them are equally part of the human situation today. Hence it may seem that there is something in the universe which prompts these questions; that it belongs to the character of the universe to elicit wonder; and that to understand anything of its character we must not exclude wonder, but seek to follow it, as it were, to its source.

CHAPTER IV

Nature Displayed

I have been speaking of the world of nature in the ordinary way, as though it were quite simply 'out there', entirely objective and external. But what modern science finds 'out there' is not the nature we perceive, but a complex of energies, woven into particles and waves. The world of nature arises for us only when these energy-patterns send impulses through our senses to our brains.

The relation between the 'out there' and what we perceive is of course a very old philosophical problem. One view is that the senses receive and transmit 'information' about the external world, and that from the resulting code of nerve-impulses the brain builds up the pictures we perceive. But in what sense would 'out there' still exist if there were no human consciousness to perceive it? There would be the complex of energies, the particles and the waves: but it does not seem very meaningful to talk of unperceived colours, shapes, sounds, scents. What sort of entities would they be?

Alternatively, we can suppose that the senses and nerves transmit patterns of stimuli, rather than information, and that through these we are aroused and enabled to go forth, as it were, and enter into direct perceptive contact with the world outside. This is a rather simpler account of what may happen, but it has difficulties of its own; and it does not explain how the perceived world, so vivid and variegated, is related to the energy-patterns, which appear to be utterly different in character.

Common sense rebels against the idea that each single person 'creates' the external world by perceiving it. But somehow it is created and set before us, caused to display itself to our consciousness.

If I try to examine the experience of perceiving the outer world, what it suggests to me is indeed that a *display* is being shown to my consciousness. By a 'display' I mean something a little like an elaborate stage setting, but a very unusual one—three-dimensional, imbued with life and subject to perpetual change with time. How this is done I have no idea; it must depend in some fairly intimate way on the nerve-impulses which the energy-network sends through the senses to the brain. One of the functions of the energy-network would then be to act as a means of communication—slightly akin (another inadequate analogy) to the radio waves which connect a television production with television screens.

The obvious question then is—who or what is responsible for the display? The most plausible answer seems to me to be—some other forms of consciousness. The world of nature is a work of imagination which is communicated via the energy-network and our senses to our consciousness.

Of course, this is not a novel idea. It is not far removed from the ancient eastern doctrine that the world is *maya*, a kind of illusion emanating from the thoughts or dreams of the Gods; but an illusion only if it deceives—i.e. if it is regarded as having an independent existence on its own account or as being just what it appears to be. It is not an illusion if it is recognized for what it is—a work of imagination. The doctrine of *maya* has often led to contempt for the visible world; but that is a perversion of it.[1]

If now we return to look again from this point of view at evolution, we shall see the whole process as permeated with the imaginations of consciousness. Here, it seems to me, is the missing factor, the normally unknown but not unknowable X which leaves full scope for variations and natural selection, but makes some sense of the final display.

[1] For a Western philosophy of Imaginism, see Douglas Fawcett, *Zermatt Dialogues*, 1931, and *Oberland Dialogues*, 1939; also Raynor C. Johnson, *Nurslings of Immortality*, 1957.

Obviously, this way of looking at things involves some far-reaching assumptions. Let us for the moment assume only that some undefined forms of consciousness are active behind the display, creating it. And before going any further on this line, it may be best to consider another evolutionary problem—the origin of life.

In the light of the geological record, it is natural to suppose that life must have somehow originated out of matter, for the oldest rocks, representing vast stretches of time, reveal no trace of life. Hence the usual assumption is that when matter had evolved from simple elements to a certain degree of complexity, it became capable of sustaining—under some particularly favourable conditions in the early days of the earth—the chemical reactions which characterize living organisms; and that in this way, by a gradual transition, matter began to manifest the phenomena of life. Something like this could perhaps have happened; it may be induced to happen one day in a laboratory. But what we habitually observe happening in everyday experience is the *reverse* process: life giving rise to dead matter—skeletal forms, organic debris of many kinds.

The natural course of life is thus to issue in dead remains—products of life in time. The earth's soil is itself a product of life; it is constantly maintained and renewed both by the decomposition of organic substances and by the activities of bacterial organisms within it. The most spectacular examples of this life-into-matter process are, perhaps, the chalk formations so familiar, for instance, in the south of England: the cliffs and downlands built up from the skeletons of myriads of marine organisms, deposited while these parts of the country were under the sea.

Iron-ore deposits, too, may have sprung from the life-processes of minute organisms, in bogs or under the sea; and something similar may apply to copper (still present in the blood of crustacea), and perhaps to some other minerals. There is some evidence for extending this interpretation a good deal further;[1] but obviously one cannot suppose that the whole vast body of the earth came into being in precisely this way. However, I do not

[1] See Wilfred Branfield, *Continuous Creation*, 1950.

find it fantastic (though many people understandably may) to follow some esoteric thinkers—most notably, Rudolf Steiner—in regarding the earth as having itself been at some far distant time a kind of living organism, permeated with life-processes through and through. According to this view, the earth has undergone (and is perhaps still undergoing) an immeasurably slow process of dying, in the course of which its solid mineral substance, its skeleton, has gradually hardened into its present form.

If this were so, the geological record would have to be differently interpreted in many respects, for it would not be correct to extrapolate modern processes of earth-wear, strata-formation and so on, indefinitely into the past, and to assume that they have always occurred in very much the same way, and at more or less the same rate, as they are doing now. But there is no need to explore this part of the story in any detail here. We are concerned only with the general hypothetical picture of the living and dying earth.

If from this point of view we look back to the geological stage when the first traces of life are found, we must say that the reason why no such traces are found in earlier periods is not because the earth was dead, but just the contrary—because the earth itself was still too living to serve as the habitat of living organisms. It is precisely by dying, by becoming mineralized and relatively inert, that the earth has enabled the evolution of living forms on its surface to occur.

Where, then, does consciousness come in? According to this picture, we must say that just as life precedes matter, so does consciousness precede organic life. Consciousness is the creative basis of the whole thing: and the evolutionary process can be regarded, on the broadest scale, as the gradual involution, or incarnation, of consciousness.

The mineral kingdom, it may appear, expresses forms of consciousness, but does not embody them; in the vegetable kingdom there is a dim kind of dreaming consciousness; in animals, consciousness wakes: and in man becomes aware of itself. When vehicles capable of sustaining consciousness are brought into being, at one or other level, consciousness informs them.

CHAPTER V

The Focus of Consciousness

Perhaps it is impossible to define consciousness, except tauto-
logically as responsive awareness, but we all know what it
is—or, rather, we are inclined to assume that we know,
taking our everyday modern consciousness as the norm and regarding any variations of it as aberrations. It may be nearer the
truth to suppose that our everyday consciousness is a specialized
form of awareness, and that the senses and the brain are designed
(as Bergson and others have suggested) to keep out more than
they let in.

The well-known experiments with mescalin and lysergic acid
have shown how easily the focus of consciousness, so to speak, can
be varied to give (in many cases) a transformed picture of the
outer world; perceptions are intensified and colours and objects
seen as though glowing with inner significance.[1] Mescalin may
also introduce the subject into a wholly inner world of phantas-
magoria, sometimes agreeable, sometimes frightening.[2] If in this
latter case we say that the experience is merely a product of the
unconscious, like a dream, we have not gone far to explain it. We
cannot tell what may be coming *through* the unconscious, for we do
not know what the unconscious may be in communication with.

Similar experiences may occur, of course, without the aid of
drugs; indeed, one main reason for studying these drugs is because they produce symptoms very like those observed in certain

[1] See Aldous Huxley, *The Doors of Perception and Heaven and Hell*
(Penguin edition, 1959).

[2] See Rosalind Heywood, 'Mind and Mescalin', *Manchester Guardian*,
29 May 1954.

44

forms of mental illness: the manic-depressive syndrome, for example. But although victims of this malady obviously are mentally ill (as their behaviour shows), we are not justified in assuming that their experiences are *merely* subjective results of brain-disorder, any more than we are justified in assuming that the experiences induced by mescalin and lysergic acid are merely the subjective by-products of drug-action. It is also possible that through these changes in consciousness, however brought about, some true aspects of the world, normally hidden, are revealed.

Some support for this view is perhaps given by the fact that similar experiences may come to persons who are neither drugged nor mentally ill. An experience of heightened consciousness, with *some* points of resemblance to the mescalin phenomena, has been recounted by a scientist, the late Dr. Sherwood Taylor:

'Two years ago, in a clear, sunny autumn morning, I had walked into the gardens of St. John's College, Oxford; the dahlias were still in bloom and the Michaelmas daisies were covered with great butterflies—tortoise-shells, fritillaries and red admirals. Suddenly I saw the whole scene take on a new figure. Every plant assumed a different and *intelligible* pattern, an individuality with a meaning that was the plant itself, which, by existing in that pattern was turned towards God and praising him. So with the butterflies; they were not merely lowly organisms, but intensely alive, clad in the livery of God, and in a fashion more personal than the plants who were praising Him too. The world was a prayer and I, fallen man, was the only being whose prayer was weak and broken. For there was nothing in my heart but love and tears and the avowal, "Lord, I am not worthy." Then I knew what was meant by "O ye works of the Lord, bless ye the Lord; praise him and magnify Him for ever", for I saw that praise. So I understood what Blake meant by,

> *How do you know but ev'ry Bird that cuts the airy way*
> *Is an immense world of delight, clos'd by your senses five?*

And I saw what was meant by his saying: "If the doors of perception were cleansed, everything would appear to man as it is, infinite."

'At the same time everything revealed itself as interconnected. There was no visible link, yet round each centre of life there was an influence, as if each living thing were a centre in a spiritual medium. The vision failed after about half-an-hour, and though it has never fully returned, yet when my mind is recollected and my heart at rest, I can see the world of living things differently, and as partaking of that hidden life. Then I know that the scientific description of nature is as jejune as the chemical analysis of the painting of an old master. And, if the power of seeing nature thus is, as one may suppose, nothing to do with the power to write of it, how many millions must have lived and died in its consolation, unknown to the world? We have no right to dismiss this faculty as a rare one. It may be expressed by few, known by many, innate in all.'[1]

Another personal experience is briefly narrated in some unpublished notebooks bequeathed to me by a great-aunt, the late Sister Ivy, an Anglican anchoress:

'I saw the earth and sea as (I suppose) they may perhaps appear to the eye of a purely animal mind. It was hideous. It looked like a piece of clumsy mechanism; no gradations of colour; everything harsh, crude, and as though made by mechanical means. And, curiously enough, I saw the incoming of the tide as (I am told) it really comes—as a scientific fact, not as it appears to come. The water did not roll in; it vibrated vertically, and rose and fell like a stage sea.'

These experiences are of course only two contrasting notes in an immense scale, embracing many varieties of heightened perception of the outer world and extending over a wide mystical range in which the outer world may play no part. Many experiences from the nearer parts of the scale are on record; they may come to quite ordinary people who have not sought them.[2] Some writers draw a sharp distinction between 'nature mysticism' and mysticism of a more definitely religious kind,[3] but I doubt if this distinction is necessary and in any event it need not be

---

[1] *The Fourfold Vision*, 1945.
[2] See Raynor C. Johnson, *Watcher on the Hills*, 1959.
[3] See R. C. Zaehner, *Mysticism, Sacred and Profane*, 1957.

discussed here. I am taking the two experiences I have quoted as examples simply of how slight variations of consciousness may give two different pictures of the world—different both from the normal picture and from each other.

The two pictures seem to lie a little way on opposite sides of the norm—one on what might be called the heightened, or participating, side; the other on the lowered, or detached, side. A characteristic of the first picture is that it is lit as it were from within, and that the person concerned feels himself to be intimately related to its significance. In the second picture there is no inner light, and the person concerned felt that she was looking at something quite apart from and indeed alien to herself.

I think the two pictures have a certain bearing on the two cultures, the old and the new. The first picture points back to a mode of consciousness which was once familiar, and from which the old culture drew its original inspiration; the second picture may adumbrate the way in which the world *could* come to be commonly perceived in some future epoch, if certain tendencies in the new culture were to be carried to an extreme. For the second picture brings to the point of actual experience something implied in the scientific view of the processes of nature as soulless and determinate, indifferent and alien to the aspirations of man. Hence, in order to examine further the question of the two cultures, we must look at them as expressions of stages in the evolution of consciousness, an evolution that is still going on.

The idea that consciousness evolves is not generally recognized, which may seem rather surprising in an age permeated with evolutionary concepts. They are applied to the kingdoms of nature, to forms of society, even to galaxies, but human consciousness is supposed not to have changed appreciably since it first dawned. Yet we know that the focus of consciousness can be changed, both under the influence of drugs and on other well-attested occasions; and there is evidence, I believe, to suggest that after the physical evolution of man had come (apparently) to an end, a slow evolutionary change in the focus of human consciousness set in.

By the evolution of consciousness I mean a constant-direction change in the normal experience of the perceived world. Today the norm lies somewhere between the two examples of changed focus that I have cited. Now suppose that the norm were shifted a little way towards the heightened extreme (as it perhaps may be, quite naturally and often, in some artists). The effect would be to make the world appear more significant, more symbolic, more inclined to 'speak'. But 'symbolic' is a tricky word: if I say that a tree begins to appear symbolic I do not mean that it begins to stand for some other definable thing or definable idea. That is allegory, or picture-language—as when one might say, 'The hoary oak, like a venerable old man.' By a *symbol* in this context I mean something perceptible—it may be an object, or a string of words, or a piece of music—which carries overtones of meaning that are experienced but cannot be precisely expressed. Poetry is symbolic in this sense; hence a poem cannot be translated (though a new poem, conveying in another language something of the experience given by the original poem, can be written and sometimes has been). The overtones cannot be exactly seized and expressed, because they are not apprehended by the conscious mind alone; they resonate in the unconscious.

This experience of the world as symbolic is what we find not only in abnormal states of modern consciousness, but also in the normal consciousness of primitive peoples. They are not, as we usually are, detached observers of a passive, 'silent' world; they participate in it and it constantly 'speaks' to them, conveying impressions that are often taken to be omens, good or bad. Their *interpretation* of the primary experience may be a quite conscious process, governed by superstitious rules and traditions; it is then rather like an endeavour to translate poetry, and equally invalid. But this does not mean that the original experience, the response to the symbolic language spoken by the outer world, is merely a subjective fantasy, any more than the response to poetry is merely a projection of subjective feelings or notions on to the words.

These experiences, when primitive peoples tell of nature speaking to them or spirits speaking through nature, have often been regarded as projections of some kind, conscious or unconscious,[1] but this explanation usually fails to distinguish between the experience and the interpretation of it. Certainly the unconscious is involved in the experience—for this springs from a relationship between some elements in nature and the human unconscious— and the unconscious response may enter into and influence the character of the experience, but I think 'projection' is the wrong word for what is a two-way process of communication, or communion.[2]

Can we take the experiences of primitive peoples today as illustrations of the kind of consciousness which was normal in the early days of mankind? It would certainly be rash to assume that we have here an exact survival of early modes of consciousness; for one thing, the examples of primitive consciousness still extant are seldom free from contamination by modern influences, and they are liable to become contaminated and distorted by the very fact of being studied and recorded by modern anthropologists. But it is reasonable to suppose that they offer some indication of how the world was experienced a few thousand years or more ago.

Among the primitive societies of which we have any knowledge, there seem to be none without some form of culture and religious life. The Australian aborigines, on the bedrock of material poverty, have (or had before the white men came) a subtly articulated social system and a complex pattern of religious beliefs and rites. They also have legends of a much earlier time, the Dreamtime (*Alcheringa*), when the gods came to earth in totemic guise and life was visionary and supernatural through and through.

[1] In the strict sense of the term, projection is always unconscious. By 'conscious projection' I mean the making-up of stories and attaching them to nature in order to account for natural phenomena. This is how it used to be thought that 'animism' had arisen.

[2] 'Formerly it was thought, for example, that the symbolic perception of a tree involved an outward projection of an inward something; one projected a psychic image upon the tree, the object outside. But this thesis has proved untenable, although it seemed plausible to the ego consciousness of modern man, who experiences the one world as split into an inside and an outside.' Erich Neumann, *Art and the Creative Unconscious*, 1959.

Similar legends and myths are widespread: their common characteristic is that they tell of a descent or decline from divine beginnings. There appear to be few myths, if any, which tell of the rise of man from an ape-like condition. I am not disputing that in one sense this rise occurred; but the reason why it has not impressed itself on communal memory may be that it does not apply to consciousness. The memory of the myths is that consciousness has contracted; and had begun to do so even when the myths were born.

There is some independent evidence pointing in the same direction. The evolution of language, for instance, shows a long slow process whereby words have changed gradually from symbols into labels. For example, 'wind' and 'breath' are now labels, or nearly so, for distinct entities: not quite, for we still speak in a metaphorical way of a 'breath of wind' and of 'wind' in the stomach. 'Spirit' is also little more than a label, with the difference that we are not at all sure what, if anything, it is a label for. But in St. John's Gospel the same Greek word, *pneuma*, is employed in the story of Nicodemus (Chapter III) both where it is said that 'the wind bloweth where it listeth' and where it is said, 'so is every one that is born of the Spirit'. This usage points to a time when 'pneuma' brought an experience of something that was not precisely our wind, or breath, or spirit, but carried overtones of all three.[1]

More generally, we can say that early language was in itself more poetic (i.e. symbolic) than any modern language is; it was also more song-like, conveying differences of meaning (as many non-European languages still do) by 'tones', or variations in pitch. It went with a state of consciousness to which the world spoke in a similar symbolic way; a consciousness giving a sense of immediate participation in the life and meaning of nature which we have largely lost. (One reason for the 'difficulty' of modern

[1] On the evolution of language, see Owen Barfield, *Poetic Diction* (revised edition, 1952) and *History in English Words* (revised edition, 1954). On the evolution of consciousness generally, see the same author's *Saving the Appearances*, 1957. I am greatly in debt to these books.

poetry is that the poet has to wrestle with so many words which, in becoming useful labels, have lost their original overtones.)

But there has been gain as well as loss. That is the essential feature of the evolution of consciousness: a gain in clarity and precision and objectivity is accompanied by a loss of participation. We are able to study the processes of nature in fine analytical detail and thus to gain control over them, but we are strangers in a universe which has lost human meaning.

This gradual loss of participation helps to explain the fact—rather strange to us—that early peoples generally placed their Golden Age in the past. Today, in spite of current anxieties and disillusions, we still believe that the future *can* be, at any rate, a great improvement on the present. In most early civilizations the tendency was to feel just the reverse—that the passage of time inevitably brought decline, somewhat as it does in the bodily strength of the individual. In the Golden Age the gods had dwelt on earth; they had instituted conditions of harmony and had taught men the arts of peace. Because of their continuing inspiration, the first human rulers were the best. But the gods went away and even their own realm was darkened: the Twilight of the Gods cast its shadow on the earth.

Various features of this myth can be interpreted in various ways, but I think in essence it reflects truly the experience of a change, a contraction, of consciousness. A lengthier treatment of the subject would have to take into account here the initiation-teaching of the mystery religions, but very few records of it exist. All I am attempting is to offer a few fragments of evidence which suggest that an evolution—or rather involution—of consciousness has occurred, and that an appreciation of this is necessary for understanding the origins of modern science.

In some branches of science the line of descent goes, of course, a long way back—to Chaldean star-gazers, Egyptian measurers and builders. But it is only with the Greeks, around 400 B.C., that something like a modern spirit of scientific inquiry seems to emerge. With Socrates and Aristotle, we begin to know where we are. In contrast to the ancient Egyptians, obsessed with death, and to the other early peoples whose religions had an other-worldly trend, the Greeks were the first who looked with keen pleasure and curiosity on the world. But with this (as has often been noted) there went also a certain sadness. The traditional religion was passing away; the Dryads were leaving the groves and the oracles were in decline:

'Tis mute, the word they went to hear on high Dodona mountain. . . .

In the background of this Greek world, with its clear sunshine and strong colours, there was an encroaching darkness; the life of man was precarious, and death led only to a realm of hapless shades.[1]

I think all this represents a fairly well-marked stage in the evolution of consciousness; the apprehension of divine powers active in nature and in human life was fading and their place was being taken by ideas. Thus during the fifth century B.C. the visible Furies of Aeschylus gave way to the inner conscience and remorse of Euripides. The same sort of transition, but going further, is exemplified in the contrast between Plato, for whom Ideas were creative entities, existing in a transcendent realm of their own, and Aristotle, for whom ideas were indeed form-giving principles, but only in conjunction with material objects; they had no independent existence of their own.

It has been suggested that this process, whereby human think-ing emerged as an activity on its own account, no longer depen-dent on the inspiration, or in-breathing, of the gods, represented a kind of coming down of the Logos to earth; and that with the coming of Christ this actually happened, visibly and physically, on the public scene. It may also be felt that into the encroaching doubts and darkness of the ancient world there came then a new light; a light that shone *in* the darkness and was not prevailed

[1] 'The instinctive pessimism of the Greeks had a religious tinge which perhaps even the Epicureans found it hard entirely to expunge. They always felt that they were in the presence of unknown incalculable powers, and that subtle dangers lurked in human achievements and gains.' J. B. Bury, *The Idea of Progress*, 1920, p. 17.

upon by death. But the influence of Christianity was at first exercised not so much on human thinking as on the human will. It led most evidently to new ways of living and dying, which grew up as an alien element in the midst of the Graeco-Roman culture of those times.

It was not until Christianity had received imperial recognition from Constantine, in 313 A.D., that its doctrines had to be taken seriously by cultured Romans; and as time went on they inevitably acquired, under official patronage, a legalistic Roman stamp. But that is another story. Its bearing on the history of consciousness is that the Romans themselves, independently of Christianity, seem to have been the first people to think about law in purely human and civil terms: the laws of other peoples had always been traced back to some kind of divine origin.[1]

For a long time the Roman laws were in the care of the Pontiffs, who alone were empowered to interpret them, but gradually they passed into the hands of the Praetors (senators elected to preside over the courts); and 'Cicero said that most of his contemporaries thought that the place to look for the real core of Roman legal doctrines was in the Praetorian edicts. It was an eminently concrete, matter-of-fact body of doctrines dealing with persons and things and having little to do with abstractions, with jurisprudence or with legal philosophy.'[2] In somewhat the same way as philosophical thinking came down part of the way to earth with Aristotle, law came down to earth with the Romans.

But thinking had to go through a further stage of descent, or secularization, before it could become the instrument of modern science. This stage began in Europe during the twelfth century and led to the eventual victory of Nominalism over Realism.

---

[1] The Romans had their Twelve Tables of the law, but these had not been handed down from any Sinai. They are said (on doubtful evidence) to have been engraved on tablets after a commission of three men had been sent to Greece, in 455 B.C., to study the Greek codes.

[2] F. R. Cowell, *Cicero and the Roman Republic*, Pelican, 1956.

CHAPTER VI

By Any Other Name

It is not easy for us to enter into the mood of this celebrated controversy, which engaged some of the finest minds in Europe and lasted for about 200 years. The debate first became prominent towards the eleventh century, but the essential question had been raised much earlier by Boethius in his translation of Porphyry's Introduction to the Categories of Aristotle.[1] It concerned the status of 'universalia'—concepts which identify something ('redness', for example) which is common to a number of otherwise dissimilar objects. Boethius had asked whether the universals are things (*res*), or only names (*nomina*). In other words, is there, say, a supersensible 'redness' from which all red objects derive their colour, or is 'redness' simply the name or label we give to the quality shared by all such objects?

To most people today the answer seems obvious, but it was not so in the early Middle Ages. Realism had behind it the great authority of Plato, and it was generally favoured by the Church. For if men came to feel sure that universals had no independent existence, they would be dangerously on the way to denying the existence of other spiritual entities, or even of God. Platonism was evidently much closer to Christianity; and St. Anselm, a leading Realist, went so far as to equate God with the Platonic idea of the Good.

The controversy was thus not merely about words and

---

[1] Aristotle was of course not a Nominalist in the medieval sense, but he sowed the seeds of Nominalism with his anti-Platonic teaching about 'ideas'.

meanings; it was fundamentally about the capacities of the human mind. Could human thinking penetrate the veil of appearance and lay hold of spiritual realities, or was it restricted to studying and naming the objects of sense?

A great centre of Platonic studies during the early part of the twelfth century was the school of Charrtes; but most of its leading figures, Fulbert, Thierry, Bernard Sylvestris, Gilbert de la Porre, are shadowy, and their extant writings have a mystical-symbolical flavour which makes them uncongenial to the modern mind. Here an old tradition and discipline, linking Christianity through Plato with the best of the ancient Mysteries, was in its last flower. Its teachings soon disappeared from the public scene, but the impulse behind them continued underground and will perhaps revive in other forms, when Nominalism has had its day.

The first conflict between Realism and Nominalism led in the early thirteenth century to a kind of compromise: for a time the 'moderate Realism' of Duns Scotus and St. Thomas Aquinas prevailed. Aquinas, it appeared, had safely reconciled the teachings of Aristotle with those of the Church. But the clear demarcation he drew between faith and reason was in fact dangerous. He indeed taught that reason was by itself able to establish the existence of God; but this demarcation meant that the highest spiritual truths were accessible only to faith, and that any hope of coming to know them through a development of inner vision was in vain.

One might wonder whether, if St. Thomas had lived longer, he would have modified his doctrine on this point. In December, 1273, a few months before his death, 'while brother Thomas was saying his Mass one morning, in the chapel of St. Nicholas at Naples, something happened which profoundly affected and altered him. After Mass he refused to write or dictate; indeed he put away his writing materials. He was in the third part of the *Summa,* at the questions on penance. And brother Reginald, seeing that he was not writing, said to him: "Father, are you going to give up this great work, undertaken for the glory of God and to enlighten the world?" But Thomas replied: "Reginald, I cannot go on." Then Reginald, who began to fear that much study might have affected his master's brain, urged and insisted that he should continue his writing; but Thomas only answered in the same way. . . . After much of this urgent questioning and insisting, Thomas at last said to Reginald: "Promise me, by the living God almighty and by your loyalty to our Order and by the love you bear to me, that you will never reveal, as long as I live, what I shall tell you.' Then he added: "All that I have written seems to me like straw compared with what has now been revealed to me." '[1]

One might perhaps wonder also whether these words were altogether compatible with St. Thomas's well-known dictum, 'Nothing exists in the intellect unless first in the senses.' In any event, the practical consequence of the demarcation between faith and reason was to separate the sacred from the secular. It inclined ordinary men to feel that the mysteries of religion were beyond human grasp; eventually this led to Sunday church-going as an insurance policy, with the rest of the week agreeably free for material pursuits. More immediately, the effect was to expose 'moderate Realism' to a renewed Nominalist attack.

This came with William of Occam, best known for his 'razor': *Entia non sunt multiplicanda praeter necessitatem*[2]—an economy principle which continues to be respected by modern science. (It is obviously sensible, but a good deal depends on how *necessitatem* is interpreted.) Some of Occam's writings, with their insistence that science has to do not with 'things' but with concepts, are indeed curiously prophetic of some current views on what science is and does—i.e. that it is concerned not with 'what' anything ultimately is or with 'why' it exists, but with establishing a formal order of concepts, preferably mathematical, which correspond to

[1] From the evidence given by Lord Bartholomew of Capua, Chancellor and Pronotary of the kingdom of Sicily, at the first canonization inquiry, Naples, 1319. See *The Life of St. Thomas Aquinas: Biographical Documents*, translated and edited by Kenelm Foster, O.P., 1959.

[2] 'One should not postulate the existence of more entities than are strictly necessary'—or, other things being equal, the simplest hypothesis is to be preferred.

the structure of nature and thus enable the operation of natural processes to be fyrmally understood, predicted, and utilized.

William of Occam died in 1349. After him, Realism withdrew, so to speak, into the cloister. The 'moderate' Thomist version of it was maintained and developed by the Dominicans, but for most practical purposes the great debate was over; Nominalism had won.

Of course this brief account of the debate has been very inadequate and superficial; detailed accounts can easily be found in histories of medieval philosophy. But these, it seems to me, are inadequate in another way: they take no account of the history of human consciousness. They assume that the debate was solely about opinions, not about ways of apprehending the world. I believe the debate occurred when it did mainly because these centuries were a time when the evolution of consciousness was going through a particular phase; the last remains of the old, symbolic mode of apprehension were, in general, passing away, to appear henceforward only in rare individuals. For although evolution may be regarded over a long term as a continuous process, the evidence suggests that in both the biological and psychological fields there are periods when the process is relatively active and periods when it is relatively quiescent. *Natura nihil facit per saltum* is only half the truth.

CHAPTER VII

Every Man an Island

The victory of Nominalism over Realism was thus an early symptom of the great change in consciousness which marked the passing of the Middle Ages in Europe and the onset of our modern epoch. Its essential notes were an enhanced selfconsciousness, leading to a new emphasis on individualism and a new demand for freedom in all spheres. It came to expression gradually in the Reformation, in nationalism and capitalism, in social-revolutionary movements. In music, it led away from polyphony towards dramatic self-expression; in painting, from the visionary and the symbolic towards the use of perspective for conveying a lifelike view of the world. It liberated thinking from dependence on tradition and authority and opened the way for a science based on observation and experiment.

Of course, this new stage in the evolution of consciousness—this change in the way in which men experienced themselves and the world—did not come about everywhere at the same time; there are parts of the world where it has not happened yet. It seems to have happened first in northern and western Europe, outside the Latin countries; and the fact that it developed most strongly in England—the island of individualism where 'every man's home is his castle'—may be the fundamental reason why England took the lead in science and industry during the centuries ahead.

In physical terms, what happened was that the progressive indrawing of the self into the confines of the body—a process closely associated with the evolution of consciousness—reached a certain culmination at this time. The man of thought came into closer acquaintance with the man of bone.[1] Of course he was not consciously aware of this, but he experienced its effects. By encountering the final resistance of the physical body, so to speak, he became more sharply conscious of himself; and of himself as an individual standing apart from the world of nature and looking out objectively upon it.[2]

He was alone in his body with himself, and he looked out on a world which now appeared to him to be empty of animating spirit, a world that no longer 'spoke' of anything behind it. He was free to put any questions to it with no feeling of impiety, and to perform on it whatever operations and experiments he chose. This new freedom was exciting; it opened up immense vistas of conquest and exploration, and the explorations were indeed carried out. But this mood of confident optimism was accompanied inwardly by self-questioning and doubt.

Doubt is indeed an essential, enduring element in the new type of consciousness which began to evolve in post-medieval

---

[1] It may not be entirely far-fetched to see an unconscious projection of this happening in the widespread emergence, quite suddenly during the fifteenth century, of the 'Dance of Death' motif in western European art. France knew it as the *danse macabre*; Spain as the *danza de la muerte*; Italy as the *ballo della morte*; Germany as the *Totentanz*. We find it in paintings, murals, woodcuts, sculptures, stained-glass windows, tapestries. Generally the pictures show a skeleton greeting some living people and by implication reminding them of their mortal end. See James M. Clark, *The Dance of Death in the Middle Ages and the Renaissance*, 1950; J. Huizinga, *The Waning of the Middle Ages*, 1924, ch. xi.

[2] 'For perhaps the first time, except for reflections in the water and the dull surfaces of metal mirrors, it was possible to find an image that corresponded accurately to what others saw. Not merely in the privacy of the boudoir; in another's home, in a public gathering, the image of the ego in new and unexpected attitudes accompanied one. . . . The use of the mirror signalled the beginning of introspective biography in the modern style: that is, not as a means of edification but as a picture of the self, its depths, its mysteries, its inner dimensions. The self in the mirror corresponds to the physical world that was brought to light by science in the same epoch: it was the self *in abstracto*, only part of the real self, the part that one can divorce from the background of nature and the influential presence of other men.' Lewis Mumford, *Technics and Civilisation*, 1934.

Europe. It arises from the solitude of the individual within himself. Nothing is quite real to him unless he can himself experience it; and his capacity for going out of himself, for sharing in the experience of others or for experiencing (as distinct from observing) the outer world, is greatly reduced, for this type of consciousness is essentially an 'onlooker' one. Hence he can no longer in any strict sense 'believe', for belief implies reliance on some authority, and he cannot recognize any external authority as final. He is a 'doubting Thomas', who must either doubt or know.[1]

But have there not been doubters and sceptics in all ages? Yes, every phase in the evolution of consciousness is to some extent anticipated by exceptional individuals, and to a lesser degree sometimes by communities. The exceptional individuals are generally treated as heretics; the communities are transient. When a new phase of consciousness really sets in, it fairly soon becomes general and natural, and gradually makes its mark on all departments of life. The contrast is something like the difference between a single wave and a steady tide.

Thus in the new climate of post-medieval England we find a mixture of confidence and doubt, of liberation and anxiety. The anxiety was manifest particularly in the religious sphere. For the only religion fully congenial to the onlooker-consciousness is one that can be 'proved on the pulses' (somewhat as science depends on experiment). But this is difficult, and the early Protestants, having thrown off the authority of an infallible Church, sought for reassurance by turning to the authority of the Bible, the infallible Word. But the Bible cannot remit sins. Many of the early Protestants (especially the Puritans) were haunted by convictions of sin; and in order to earn merit, to provide themselves with evidence that they were among the elect, they turned to work. Tawney and Weber, in classic studies, have described how much this regime of diligence and thrift contributed to the

[1] In everyday usage, of course, 'belief' has various meanings. A 'doubting Thomas' may 'believe' that some event is likely to occur, which is an estimate of odds, or he may believe in the existence of something which he has never seen, but for which the evidence is accessible and overwhelming. He will never believe purely as an act of faith.

rise of a new middle-class capitalism and to the building up of wealth.

Meanwhile, science was beginning to take advantage of its liberation from medievalism. The confluence of the new wealth with the new science made possible the Industrial Revolution. We will come to this shortly, after first looking briefly at some other aspects of the new epoch in its early days.

CHAPTER VIII

Figures of Romance

The evolution of the modern onlooker-consciousness can be viewed also in terms of the relation of conscious to unconscious. Briefly, it seems that the threshold between them has hardened: thinking has become a more strictly conscious process, never of course cut off from unconscious influences but less open to them. The older type of symbolic thinking was more dreamlike; more of what is now unconscious extended into consciousness. If one pictures the unconscious as an ocean and the conscious as a small island, one might say that early man lived half in and half out of the water. We have now mostly withdrawn on to dry land; and persons who are overtaken by the tide and carried out to sea are liable to find themselves in mental hospitals.

Jung has emphasized the dangers inherent in this relative cutting off of the conscious mind from its unconscious springs: for the unconscious is still there, as potent as ever, and may stage irrational outbreaks or inspire hysterical mass movements in protest against its confinement. The inveighings of some modern writers—most obviously D. H. Lawrence—against the impoverishing influence of industrial civilization spring from an intuition similar to Jung's. The island is too dry.[1]

The early stages of this desiccating process became apparent during the seventeenth century; but they were not accepted without resistance. I think they were resisted, though not explicitly, by

---

[1] 'Our souls that once were naked to the winds of heaven are now thickly clad, and have learned to build a house and light a fire upon its hearth, and shut-to the doors and windows.' W. B. Yeats, 'Ideas of Good and Evil', from *Essays and Introductions* (Macmillan, 1961), p. 41.

Isaac Newton, who spent a great deal of time on alchemy, mysticism and the prophetic books of the Old Testament, and after he had published the *Principia*, at the age of forty-two, gave little continuous attention to science for the rest of his long life.[1]

Newton seems to me like a man who climbs a mountain pass and looks over it; on the far side is a quite unfamiliar landscape, dry and austere. He examines it and ponders on it; with a prodigious intellectual effort he maps its strange contours and measures some of the natural forces which have made it what it is. But he explores it for no longer than he can help; he prefers to live on the familiar side of the pass.

It is to the seventeenth century, also, that the celebrated phenomenon known as the 'dissociation of sensibility' has been assigned. In his well-known essay on *The Metaphysical Poets* (1921), T. S. Eliot wrote of 'something which had happened to the mind of England between the time of Donne or Lord Herbert of Cherbury and the time of Tennyson or Browning; it is the difference between the intellectual and the reflective poet. Tennyson and Browning are poets, and they think; but they do not feel their thought as immediately as the odour of a rose. A thought to Donne was an experience, it modified his sensibility. . . . In the seventeenth century a dissociation of sensibility set in, from which we have never recovered; and this dissociation, as is natural, was aggravated by the influence of the most powerful poets of the century, Milton and Dryden.'

Twenty-six years later, after this dictum had come under prolonged attack from literary critics and historians, Mr. Eliot modified it. In his 1947 British Academy lecture on Milton, he said:

'I believe that the general affirmation represented by the phrase "dissociation of sensibility" . . . retains some validity; but . . . to lay the burden on the shoulders of Milton and Dryden was a mistake. If such a dissociation did take place, I suspect that

---

[1] The surviving manuscripts on alchemy in Newton's handwriting are said to run to some 650,000 words. No doubt he thought it prudent to give up his alchemical experiments on becoming Master of the Mint.

the causes are too complex and profound to justify our accounting for it in terms of literary criticism. All we can say is, that something like this did happen; that it had something to do with the Civil War; that it would be unwise to say that it was caused by the Civil War, but that it is a consequence of the same cause which brought about the Civil War; that we must seek the causes in Europe, not in England alone; and for what these causes were, we may dig and dig until we get to a depth at which words and concepts fail us.'

Today, Mr. Eliot's original contention has gone quite out of fashion; thus Professor Kermode advises poets to 'turn back and rediscover Milton', and 'by the time they have done that, the dissociation of sensibility, the great and in some ways noxious historical myth of Symbolism (though the attempt to see history in terms of the Image was noble) will be forgotten, except by historians crying their new categories and still unheard persuasions'.[1]

I believe that something like a 'dissociation of sensibility' did occur (though not at one fixed date), but it needs to be understood in the light of the evolution of consciousness. Donne does come into the picture, though perhaps not in quite the way that Mr. Eliot first suggested. He was well acquainted with the 'new philosophy' and made free use of images and similes drawn from the science of his time. But he seems to have felt not altogether at home in its atmosphere; and after him it became increasingly difficult for anyone to write good poetry while thinking scientifically about the world.

This was inevitable, for it is both the strength and the weakness of the onlooker-consciousness that, as it develops, thinking and feeling tend to fall apart. The strength, because detached, unemotional thinking about nature has been essential for modern science. The weakness, because response to other forms of experience is impaired.[2]

*

[1] *Romantic Image*, 1957.

[2] In a well-known autobiographical passage, Charles Darwin wrote of his regret that his mind seemed to have become nothing but 'a kind of machine for grinding general laws out of large collections of facts . . . If I had to live my life over again, I would have made a rule to read some

By the end of the eighteenth century the signs of desiccation were being quite explicitly resisted; most notably by

> *A choleric enthusiast,*
> *Self-educated* William Blake
> *Who threw his spectre in the lake,*
> *Broke off relations in a curse*
> *With the Newtonian universe,*
> *But even as a child could pet*
> *The tigers Voltaire never met,*
> *Took walks with them through Lambeth, and*
> *Spoke to Isaiah in the Strand,*
> *And heard inside each mortal thing*
> *Its holy emanation sing.*[1]

I shall resist the temptation to say much about Blake; travellers have been lost in his forest. But two points are relevant: his view of Newton and his relation to the poets of the Romantic Revival.

With Newton—'A mighty Spirit leap'd from the land of Albion, Nam'd Newton'—Blake often coupled Bacon and Locke. These pioneers of the new scientific outlook he regarded as darkeners of vision and promoters of sleep:

> *May God us keep*
> *From single vision and Newton's sleep!*

He meant the normal consciousness which perceives nothing beyond or through the world given to the senses; whereas the dominating feature of his own many-sided life was a frequent awareness of living in two worlds at once:

'Felpham is a sweet place for Study, because it is more Spiritual than London. Heaven opens here on all sides her golden Gates; her windows are not obstructed by vapours; voices of

poetry and listen to some music at least once every week; for perhaps the parts of my brain now atrophied would thus have been kept active through use. The loss of these tastes is a loss of happiness, and may possibly be injurious to the intellect, and more probably to the moral character, by enfeebling the emotional part of our nature.' *Life and Letters of Charles Darwin*, edited by his son Francis Darwin, 1887; vol. I.

[1] W. H. Auden, *New Year Letter*, 1941.

celestial inhabitants are more distinctly heard, & their forms more distinctly seen; & my cottage is also a shadow of their houses.'

I don't know if Blake would have recognized in the evolution of consciousness something familiar to him under another name (the concept of evolution was of course not current in his time), but I think he might. He believed in the declension of the world from a primal state of Innocence, a process mirrored by the fall into Experience at adolescence in individual life. And in the new scientific outlook he saw a kind of imprisonment in Experience and a blindness to its limitations.

He was not in the usual sense of the word a mystic: his visions did not carry him away into quite other realms. All through his life he was keenly and critically aware of the ordinary world around him—the coolly complacent rationalism of the upper classes accompanied in London by Hogarthian scenes of squalor and vice and a simmering threat of mob violence (as a young man of twenty-three he was caught up by chance in the Gordon riots and saw the burning of Newgate gaol). Against the social evils of his time he protested passionately,[1] but it was always clear to him that Jerusalem had to be seen before it could be built. It was hidden from single vision and revealed only to Imagination, the power which alone could open the sleeper's eyes and make transparent the prison of Experience.

This word, 'Imagination', is one of the few links between Blake and the poets of the Romantic Revival. Wordsworth, Coleridge and Shelley were all his contemporaries, and Coleridge had several talks with him, but no record of them appears to exist; the common view in Romantic circles was that Blake, though highly gifted, was mad.[2] Yet in one respect at least Coleridge had much in common with Blake; he thought and wrote a great deal about Imagination, and probably did more than anyone to give currency

[1] For this somewhat neglected radical side of Blake, and the effect on him and his livelihood of the Industrial Revolution, see J. Bronowski, *A Man Without a Mask*, 1944.

[2] But this view was not shared by some of those who had close acquaintance with him—the practically-minded Linnell, for instance, who later became a wealthy Victorian painter.

to the new meaning which the word was then beginning to acquire. In Chaucer's time it had signified a mental image, a picture arising in the mind's eye; with the Romantics (and especially with Coleridge[1]) it came to mean an actively creative faculty:

'Coleridge . . . began by dividing Imagination into two parts, Primary and Secondary. Primary Imagination he describes as "the living power and prime agent of all human perception, and a repetition in the finite mind of the eternal act of creation in the infinite 'I am' ' ". This means that even the simplest act of perception is not (as the analogy of the modern camera has led most people to believe) an act of passive reception, but an act of creation, and an act, moreover, which is continuous with the divine act of creation itself. Man instinctively thinks in images because God created the world in images. This first kind of Imagination is something which is "given": it is the primeval picture-consciousness which still speaks to us in myth and saga and fairy-tale, and into which all children are born. But Secondary Imagination is something over which we have conscious control. Coleridge says we must think of it "as an echo of the former. . . . It dissolves, diffuses, dissipates *in order to recreate.*" '[2]

Coleridge also distinguished Imagination from Fancy, which merely plays with images and brings them into agreeable patterns; no new apprehension pierces through the pattern, as it does when Imagination is at work. Any such imaginative apprehension is some way short of Blake's direct vision, but it is on the same path. And although the Romantic poets did not often set their concern with Imagination over against 'Newton's sleep', I think they were moved—as was the Romantic movement generally—by a similar reaction against the new mechanistic philosophy.

*

[1] Anticipated of course by Shakespeare, in lines whose bold claim is perhaps dimmed by familiarity:

> *And as imagination bodies forth*
> *The forms of things unknown, the poet's pen*
> *Turns them to shapes, and gives to airy nothing*
> *A local habitation, and a name.*

[2] A. C. Harwood, 'The Wholeness of Imagination', in *Child and Man* annual, 1959.

Meanwhile, another contemporary figure, Goethe, was vehemently attacking certain aspects of Newtonian science, especially Newton's theory of colour. Goethe was utterly unlike Blake in most ways, but their hostility to all that Newton symbolized for them arose, I would say, from similar roots.

Until lately, the prevailing scientific opinion was that in attacking Newton's colour theory, Goethe was simply wrong-headed. His own theory, which regarded colours as emerging from the polarity between light and darkness, might be allowed a certain poetic charm, but there was nothing in it that science could get hold of. Recent studies, however, have shown that Goethe's experiments with prisms revealed some facts about coloured shadows which Newton had not observed, and indeed that Goethe came very near to establishing the modern distinction—practically important in various fields—between additive and subtractive colour-mixing.

However, it would be misleading to regard the colour-theories of Newton and Goethe as rivals, one of which could come to supersede the other for all purposes. They overlap, but in certain respects they are quite different. Newton's theory is not really a theory of *colours* at all, for colours are something we experience, and Newtonian theory in its modern form deals with wavelengths which are associated with colour perceptions but are not themselves perceived. Newton's theory might be better called a branch of his theory of optics—part of mathematical physics. Goethe's theory is genuinely a theory of colours; it interprets, and can enrich, our experience of colours, but it does not lend itself to mathematical formulation and does not lead (or not nearly so directly) to power over nature.

At present, we need Newtonian optics for some purposes; Goethe's *Farbenlehre* for others; they will be united at some future time, when science and art, and the two cultures they represent, are remarried. It may be that Goethe's remark to Eckermann will then sound less eccentric: 'As for what I have done as a poet, I take no pride whatever in it. Excellent poets have lived at the same time as myself; poets more excellent have lived before me and others will come after me. But that in my century I am the only person who knows the truth in the difficult science of colours—of that, I say, I am not a little proud, and here I have a consciousness of superiority to many.'

Goethe attacked Newton's theory first of all because it led away from the actual experience of colours into a realm of conceptual entities—'corpuscles' for Newton, wave-particles today —which can be thought about and manipulated mathematically, but are not and cannot be directly observed. By Goethe's time, moreover, scientific thinkers (or natural philosophers, as they were then called) were already treating these unobservables as the basic realities of the external world and regarding the experience of colour as a subjective affair which arose in some unknown way within the human brain. Here indeed was an early example of that general scientific trend which has produced the picture of man living in an alien, humanly meaningless universe.

Goethe was always opposed to all such tendencies; his own scientific studies and experiments (which took up much more of his time during a large part of his life than is perhaps generally realized nowadays) were inspired by a quite different attitude. In order to enter fully into this, one would need to explore the whole range of his scientific work, and particularly his botany, but that would take us too far.[1]

In old-fashioned language one might say that Goethe's aim was to 'read the book of nature'. Individual phenomena were the letters of nature's script; by combining them into words and the words into sentences he was able, he believed, to apprehend their meaning; that is, the ideas which they expressed.[2]

The faculty which opened the way to nature's ideas was called by Goethe (the phrase is perhaps untranslatable) *exakte sinnliche*

[1] See Rudolf Steiner, *Goethe as Scientist* (collected prefaces to the *National-Literatur* edition of Goethe's scientific writings, translated by O. D. Wanamaker, New York, 1950), and *Goethe's Conception of the World* (English translation, 1928); also Ernst Lehrs, *Man or Matter* (revised edition, 1958). Some other aspects of Goethe's scientific work are discussed later (Chapter XVI).

[2] Goethe recognized that this approach to nature was not unlike that of the artist, but with a difference in purpose: the aim of the artist was to give form to ideas which in nature were often imperfectly or confusedly displayed.

Phantasie; it seems somewhat akin to Coleridge's Imagination. Both men sought to discern in and through the visible phenomena of nature the creative ideas from which the phenomena arose; they both had the conviction that nature does not reveal herself, except superficially, to a merely passive observer:

> *O Lady! we receive but what we give*
> *And in our life alone does nature live.*

Blake had a similar conviction, but his vision penetrated beyond the ideas to the intelligences from which the ideas were born.

CHAPTER IX

Diverging Streams

Why did the Romantic Revival peter out, with so few of its high hopes realized?

It had arisen first as a protest against eighteenth-century artistic formalism, and especially against stereotyped poetic diction. One of Blake's 'Proverbs of Hell'—'Bring out number, weight & measure in a year of dearth'—can indeed be understood in this sense; but it can also be taken to mean, roughly, 'When Imagination fails, the measurable becomes the measure of all things.'

Against this, too—the setting up of the calculating intellect as the sole arbiter of truth—the Romantic movement was a protest; and it was a protest also against the beginnings of modern industrialism:

'The factory bell would clang at dawn and its doors would not shut for fourteen or sixteen hours. . . . Children of seven were bound to the first textile mills until they were twenty-one. . . . In the new towns many thousands lived in cellars or over cess-pits to die miserably of ague and fever.'[1] 'Cottage industry which in many counties had been associated with rural life, especially spinning, was rapidly disappearing; the cottage was poorer. With enclosure vanished common rights, and small holdings, and the labourer's plot was reduced to a cottage garden. Wages, although they rose, lagged far behind the soaring price of food. Rural poverty was far worse, and more widespread, than urban poverty.'[2]

[1] Keith Feiling, *A History of England*, 1950, p. 800.
[2] J. H. Plumb, *England in the Eighteenth Century* (Pelican), 1950.

These appalling conditions had a quite strong influence in driving the two cultures apart. Among the classically educated intelligentsia of the time, particularly at Oxford and Cambridge, they created a lasting prejudice against applied science as the ally of industrial barbarism. But the enclosures, for all their harshness, greatly increased the productivity of agriculture, and the factories were soon doing the same for manufacture. Neither the scholars nor the poets could foresee that the application of science to industry, by promoting a vast expansion in national wealth, would eventually provide the indispensable key for opening the prisons of gross poverty and epidemic disease. Any man of sensibility was bound to protest against the hideous early marks of the new capitalism; and the Romantics had good grounds for protesting also against the new scientific philosophy. They felt, with reason, that it was bringing about an impoverishment of the faculties proper to the human mind, a darkening of the 'windows of the soul'.

But of these various protests, only the protest against literary formalism was effective. Here, on their own ground, the Romantics were free to express their feelings and to attempt at least to illustrate their ideas. But the ideas themselves, and especially the idea of Imagination, had very little influence on contemporary thought and none at all on the rising new scientific outlook.

One reason for this was that most of their ideas (except Blake's) suffered, it seems to me, from a certain persistent vagueness. Shelley could write of Imagination in a phrase that Blake might almost have used: 'Imagination is as the immortal God which should assume flesh for the redemption of mortal passion.' Yet one may wonder whether these words had an entirely clear meaning even for Shelley himself; whereas if Blake had used them he would have known exactly what *he* meant by them, though he might have had difficulty in making others see it.

As Mr. Owen Barfield has put it, the question that needed to be answered was, 'In what *way* is Imagination true?'[1] It was a question implicit in Goethe's scientific method; he came near to grappling with it; but (unlike Coleridge) he disliked 'thinking

[1] *Romanticism Comes of Age*, 1944.

about thinking', and it is perhaps not quite clear what sort of existence he attributed—for instance—to his *Urpflanze*, or archetypal plant, or how his *exakte sinnliche Phantasie* was related to the ordinary powers of the mind.

If Coleridge had combined with his rare philosophical gifts a firmer character and a greater capacity for ordering and finishing his writings, he might have gone a long way towards answering the question by developing his account of Imagination into a fruitful theory of knowledge. But in his *Biographia Literaria* the chapter headed 'Nature of Imagination' breaks off after about two pages. So the question never was answered, and the science of the time went its own way, actively engaged in building up its armoury of practically effective truths of a different kind.

Another reason why the Romantic movement had so little lasting influence outside its own literary-artistic field is that, although it came before the world as a youthful gesture of revolt, it was in a sense reactionary: it tended to look for its inspiration in the past. It dreamt of an ideal age, long ago (Rousseau's 'noble savage' and Blake's 'Druids', though rather incongruous companions, both belong to this dream); its writers (including Blake and Goethe) were very ready to welcome and admire the pseudo-Ossian epics of James Macpherson; it cultivated a 'Gothic' style in its paintings and in some of its feebler literary productions.

Yet this nostalgia for the past was not altogether unjustified; the development of the modern consciousness does represent from one point of view a loss, a decline; it is part of the working out of the 'Fall of man'. But if one believes that the rise of the modern scientific outlook is both a necessary and a potentially beneficial stage in human evolution, the loss will not be simply deplored, nor will any attempt to recover older forms of consciousness be applauded. The point is to understand what has been happening, and to see in perspective both loss and gain.

Nowadays it is the loss that needs to be emphasized, for it is seldom recognized, or only nostalgically and romantically, and is then not clearly understood. The prevailing assumption is that the modern outlook has come about by steady ascent from the darkness of ignorance and the twilight of superstition. Hence the scientific way of looking at the world is regarded as a culmination; an emergence at last into clear, rational, reliable daylight.

This, too, is only part of the truth. In becoming sharper, the focus of consciousness has narrowed: a wide diffused illumination has given way to a small bright beam. Within its circle of light everything is seen with unprecedented analytical fineness; but the circle excludes a great deal that was once apprehended and is now generally unrecognized or unknown.

In other words, the consciousness which has produced modern science—a relationship which helps to explain why modern science could not arise before it did—is a highly specialized mode of apprehension which belongs particularly to our epoch and will be transcended in time.[1]

Something very similar is true of those contemporary movements in philosophy—Logical Atomism, Logical Positivism, Linguistic Analysis—which are the direct heirs of Nominalism. They have done valuable and necessary work in demolishing some of the vaguely cloud-capped towers of nineteenth-century Idealism, and in promoting a new clarity and rigour in philosophical discourse.[2] But it should not be assumed that they have therefore made nonsense of all previous metaphysics and established absolute new standards of verifiable truth. The standards they have established are those that correspond to the particular form of consciousness which in our epoch is reaching a certain extreme. If the focus got much narrower, human consciousness might lose its human character.

---

[1] As long as the world could be experienced as a living organism, still imbued (if obscurely) with the divine creative forces of its origin—or as long even as a strong tradition of that experience persisted—it was not only felt to be impious to seek for knowledge by dissecting nature: there was little incentive to do so, for it was assumed that any knowledge obtainable from such an approach would be unimportant—irrelevant to essential human concerns.

[2] For a short survey of these movements, see G. J. Warnock, *English Philosophy Since 1900*, 1958.

74

Some of the main concepts used in metaphysics derive ultimately (as do many of the concepts in theology), not from inven-
tive thinking, but from experience; or, perhaps more exactly,
from symbols which could once be experienced. The same kind
of thing has happened to them as happened to words. They have
dried out into abstract ideas, just as words have dried out from
symbols into labels. The ideas continued to be manipulated, to
be thought *about*, long after they had ceased to be experienced.
Modern philosophers are thus quite right in finding them mostly
meaningless; they have lost their meaning. But they had it once,
when a form of consciousness capable of experiencing them, of
apprehending them symbolically, was still prevalent. They were
fitted then to act as the vehicles of a certain kind of knowledge—
not the exact, analytical, strictly conscious knowledge characteristic of modern science, but genuine in its own way.

The Romantic Revival illustrates that divergence between art
and science which has deepened into the gulf between the two cultures today. One further example of divergence, more closely
related to the origins of modern science, comes from a pursuit
which was dying when the Romantic Revival began.

CHAPTER X

The Alchemists

Alchemy may have originated in China or India, or possibly in Egypt, long before Christ; the European tradition of it goes back through the Arabs to the Greeks of Alexandria, early in the Christian era. It seems to have started there as a practical search for ways of making gold; it acquired mystical aspects a good deal later, mainly under Christian influence. Finally, in Europe, it became almost wholly mystical—disappearing as it were into the empyrean around the end of the seventeenth century, at the time when the new atomic chemistry, foreshadowed by Gassendi and Boyle, was approaching to take over its earthly territory.

During its European heyday, in the thirteenth and fourteenth centuries, the serious alchemists may have been outnumbered by confidence-trickster charlatans. But there were plenty of serious alchemists; they were not regarded as cranks but as men learned in the science of their day; and in the terms of that science they had no reason to doubt that the transmutation of metals was possible.

They had translations of Arabic works on the subject, and they were familiar with Aristotle's doctrine of 'matter' and 'forms'. (This had no original connection with alchemy, but it had great influence on the theory and practice of alchemy later on.) The alchemists accordingly believed that substances were made up of a primal matter—the same for all of them—and of 'forms', or formative principles, which gave each substance its particular character. Hence, in order to change one metal into another, all that was necessary was to cause it to part with its 'form'—a kind of death—and to infuse it with a new 'form'—a kind of rebirth.'

It was obvious, however, that new growth proceeded not from substances themselves, but from seeds, and it was thought that when seeds were sown in the earth, they actually decayed and died before the resurrection of new growth could begin. Hence the alchemist sought for means of distilling from gold its 'seed', after which he hoped to infuse the 'seed' into another metal, first reduced to a primal condition by some kind of 'putrefaction' or dissolution. Thus the necessary conditions would be provided for the resurrection of the metal into pure gold.

This is of course a grossly simplified account of procedures which had all sorts of intricate ramifications and variations. Some alchemists, for instance, believed that the *pneuma*, or spiritual breath, which sustained all created things, had to be drawn into the operation if it was to succeed. And the search for ways of making gold soon developed, of course, into a search for the famous 'philosopher's stone', the magical substance which would not only effect transmutations but would heal disease and lengthen life (though the search for the 'elixir of life', conferring some kind of immortality, seems to have belonged more to Chinese alchemy than to its Western versions). There was a strong tradition that the final secret concerning the making and nature of the stone could be learnt only verbally, from someone—perhaps an older friend or perhaps a mysterious stranger—who had himself received it in the same way and was willing to impart it only to a person who gave proof that he was worthy of it. Without this secret—a kind of initiation into the inner mysteries of alchemy—it was impossible to understand the recipes. If there was any such secret, it was apparently well kept; no record of it seems to have survived.[2]

★

[1] The modern chemist does something not quite unlike this when he changes one substance into another by altering its molecular structure. His 'primal matter' is energy; his 'forms' are atomic-molecular patterns.

[2] 'As late as 1653, Elias Ashmole, the great English antiquarian, records in his diary with rejoicing that William Backhouse, "lying sick in Fleet-Street, over against St. Dunstan's Church, and not knowing whether he

Alchemy, however, is another jungle, full of controversial obscurities; I shall touch here on only two aspects of it—the experience of the alchemist in his laboratory and his attitude towards the material world.

Many alchemical operations were very elaborate and long: we hear of a substance being distilled and redistilled 700 times over, and of fires that had to be kept going at a fairly even heat for months or even years. Often, no doubt, the exciting hope of at last achieving success was enough to sustain almost any amount of patience. But it seems evident from the writings of alchemists that for them the watching of chemical reactions was in itself an absorbing experience—quite different from anything normally experienced in a modern laboratory. Boiling and bubbling, melting and congealing, vaporizing and distilling, the precipitation of a substance out of a turbid liquid, changes in colour and density —these processes are seldom of great interest in themselves for the modern chemist; they are merely steps towards the final result, preferably a quantitative one. For the alchemist, the qualitative changes were the main thing. They were a language he sought to read, and in reading it he felt that he was learning something of how spiritual powers operated in nature and in man. But it was a language capable of various interpretations, and how he interpreted it depended on his cast of mind and on his purpose.

If he was concerned only with transmuting metals, or with the more ambitious hope of preparing the philosopher's stone, the changes indicated whether the work was proceeding on the right lines. According to a widely accepted tradition, the metal had first to decay into a black, formless mass, afterwards turning white and finally red. 'Thou shalt have a sparkling red, like unto the flaming fire. Then art thou come indeed to thy Harvest, and to the end of all thy Operations.'[1]

If he were mystically minded—as many alchemists certainly were, especially in the later periods of the art—he could readily

should live or die, about eleven o'clock told me in syllables the true matter of the Philosopher's Stone, which he bequeathed to me as a legacy."'
F. Sherwood Taylor, *The Alchemists*, 1951.

[1] G. Starkey, *Ripley Reviv'd*, 1678. Quoted by R. D. Gray, *Goethe the Alchemist*, 1952.

see in this colour sequence a picture of the fall of man into the darkness of sin, his purification, and at last the sunrise of his redemption. And not only colour-changes, but other chemical processes, spoke to him in a similar strain. 'The combination of two bodies he saw as *marriage*, the loss of their characteristic activity as *death*, the production of something new as a *birth*, the rising up of vapours as a *spirit leaving the corpse*, the formation of a volatile solid as the making of a *spiritual body*. These conceptions influenced his idea of what should occur, and he therefore decided that the final end of the substances operated on should be analogous to the final end of man—a soul in a new, glorious body, with the qualities of clarity, subtlety and agility.'[1] He may perhaps have felt that by watching these processes, by entering deeply into them with a devotion of thought and feeling, he was working also on himself.

But not always on himself alone. Even more closely bound up with alchemy, perhaps, was the idea that the entire material creation was in a fallen state and seeking redemption. 'By this crafte alle metailles that growen of myne and been corrupte and inparfite been brought and tournyd fro ynperfection to perfection.'[2] Or, more generally, 'the alchemical process was a small illustration or example of the whole purpose of things, which were impelled to seek perfection by their striving towards the perfect ideas of their kind in God.'[3]

This is one reason why alchemical writings are so obscure. It is often impossible to say whether the alchemist is describing a reaction he has actually witnessed, or using chemical terms in a symbolical, mystical sense: a distinction which was probably much less clear-cut to him than it is to us. Also it may be that among the alchemists were men who had retained something of an older consciousness—the kind of consciousness to which the outer world 'spoke' habitually in a symbolic way. This may be why they sometimes wrote of witnessing various chemical effects

[1] F. Sherwood Taylor, op. cit.
[2] *Semita Recta*, attributed to Albertus Magnus. Quoted by John Read, *Prelude to Chemistry*, 1936.
[3] F. Sherwood Taylor, op. cit.

which would not be expected to occur in the course of the operations they describe: they may have actually seen more than would be evident to modern eyes.

There is no doubt, at any rate, that the alchemists approached their experiments in a mood far removed from the detached, objective scrutiny required by modern science. And it was when this mood changed, together with the fading out of the older type of consciousness, that practical alchemy came to an end. The watching of chemical experiments was no longer in itself an absorbing experience. So alchemy underwent a kind of fission, giving rise on the one hand to a mystical Hermetic philosophy (in the writings of Thomas Vaughan, for instance),[1] and on the other to the beginnings of modern chemistry.

These were necessary developments, but they illustrate the kind of divergence which was later to separate the two cultures: one line of study becoming less practical and tending to draw its nourishment from the past, the other turning to quantitative investigations which would powerfully shape the future.[2]

We have been looking from various angles at the change in consciousness—in ways of apprehending and thinking about the world—which led into our modern epoch. Now we will look ahead at some of the consequences which the character and outlook of modern science could have for culture and religion and social life.

[1] See also Mary Anne Atwood, *A Suggestive Inquiry into the Hermetic Mystery*; London, 1850; Belfast, 1918.

[2] 'Philosophy, with the aid of experience, has at length banished the study of alchymy; and the present age, however desirous of riches, is content to seek them by the humbler means of commerce and industry.' Gibbon, *Decline and Fall*, vol. 1, chap. 13 (1776).

CHAPTER XI

Look to the Earth

There was one element in alchemy which might still be valuable. The alchemists believed that man had a certain responsibility towards the material world; a responsibility to co-operate in the process of redemption or regeneration which was God's purpose not only for man but for all created things.

This is clearly a difficult conception, not acceptable to modern science in those terms.[1] But there is nothing recondite in the idea that man has a responsibility towards the earth which sustains him and supplies his bodily wants. This should not be foreign to science, which lives by exploring the material world and learning to control it. Yet the period which has seen the triumphant rise of modern science has also been the period of the 'rape of the earth'; of the exploitation of the earth's natural resources on an altogether unprecedented scale. May not our descendants look back with amazement at the prodigality with which we have lifted irreplaceable minerals and ores and oil out of the earth, besides making vast inroads on its forests and cultivable land and turning some fertile areas into huge dust-bowls—all in not much over a

---

[1] Perhaps there is some indication of it in the Bible, which begins with the story of a garden and ends with the vision of a city. Adam in Eden has not entered into material existence as we know it; he has not come up against the recalcitrance of matter and the hard labour it requires. Nor is the city, the new Jerusalem, made of matter as we know it; it is built of 'pure gold, like unto clear glass'. Adam is exiled from the garden of Innocence to the stony ground of Experience; the city suggests a third term in the sequence, a condition for which we have no name.

century? But a great deal has been written on this aspect of the subject; I need not enlarge on it.[1]

True, it is not scientists themselves, but commercial exploiters and bad farmers, who have done most of the damage. Again, it is not so much pure science as its child, technology, which has supplied the tools. But the voice of science has seldom been raised in protest. More often the complaint is that the resources of science are not being properly used to reduce poverty by increasing the earth's yield. Obviously there is great need for better measures to cope with present poverty and malnutrition and with the perhaps not very distant threat of famine from too many people and not enough food. Obviously, too, there is nothing wrong in principle with using scientific methods to develop and harvest the resources of the earth. The distinction is between good husbandry and bad.

Nature, left to herself, achieves an ecological balance in all sorts of climates and environments, but often at a low level of harvestable yield. Good husbandry raises the yield, but without destroying the ecological balance, which implies the continued health and fertility of soil and animals and should contribute to the health of man himself. Bad husbandry can also raise the yield, and for a time may raise it faster and further than good husbandry will, but at the long-term cost of impaired fertility, the multiplication of pests and of plant and animal ailments,[2] and

[1] See, inter alia, G. V. Jacks and R. O. Whyte, The Rape of the Earth, 1939; Michael Roberts, The Estate of Man, 1951; Fairfield Osborn, Our Plundered Planet, 1949, and The Limits of the Earth, 1954; Edward Hyams, Soil and Civilisation, 1952; Jorian Jenks, From the Ground Up, 1950; and The Stuff Man's Made Of, 1959.

[2] 'About a hundred different pests all over the world have now developed resistance to various modern insecticides. New pests have appeared; some beneficial species have been decimated, and many biologists are beginning to feel that chemical methods of pest control are raising almost as many problems as they solve. . . . Little is known of the relation between pests and plants. Nor is the action of many insecticides understood. With better understanding of these problems, quite new control methods might emerge, and existing insecticides could be used with more subtlety. At present, they seem to be being used as very blunt instruments which are rapidly becoming blunter.' Science Correspondent of The Observer, 4 October 1959.

probably a decline in the health value of foodstuffs. One example of this tendency is the widespread, uncontrolled use of poisonous sprays on fields and orchards;[1] kindred examples are the breeding and feeding methods employed to obtain very high yields or specialized characters in livestock; and also, I think, (though this is more controversial) the constant application of large doses of artificial fertilizers as an alternative to slower organic methods of maintaining and enhancing the health and fertility of the soil.[2]

Some of these various dangers are of course well recognized: and science learns by correcting its own mistakes. It would be foolish to assume that because the first century of scientific agriculture has had some deplorable results, these will always continue. The odds are that most of the more obvious mistakes *will* be corrected: science may well have great success in reversing soil erosion, controlling pests, and raising yields sufficiently to keep populations and food supplies in balance.[3] But can we be sure that the food produced will be in every way as healthy and nourishing as food produced by older methods, or by organic methods today? This will not be easy to determine; no scientific tests of *quality* in food are at present available, and there may be quality factors not amenable to quantitative measurement. It is not a question only of physical health; the mind and spirit are influenced by choice and quality of food. Hence one cannot judge the merits of a particular method of farming solely in terms of output. A triumphantly productive world agriculture might still

[1] 'Britain's bee population is being decimated, Sir Walter Fergusson Hannay, President of the Hertfordshire Bee Keepers' Association, said when he opened the National Honey Show in London yesterday. He described the bee as the "farmer's best friend" in the matter of pollination, and said it had a host of new enemies. "I am told that the latest method of spraying by aircraft has caused the destruction of whole apiaries." ' *The Times*, 2 October 1959.

[2] Fertilizer methods have improved since it became generally accepted that separate measures (including preferably some form of organic manure) are necessary to keep up the humus content of the soil. But one objection that can still be raised against the continual use of artificials is that they are a short-cut method of feeding the plant, rather than the soil.

[3] But there must be *some* limit to the number of people the earth can feed. The amenity limit might come much sooner—unless most habitable areas are to get like Brighton on Bank Holiday.

have a deadening influence on the powers of the spirit, keeping people well fed but tending to make them a little like obedient machines.

Here we are entering a speculative region, rather remote from everyday ideas. But there are plenty of other, quite familiar ways in which modern scientific trends are causing anxiety, and they are not all associated with fear of nuclear bombs.[1] Most often, probably, they arise from a feeling that the latest tools and techniques made available by science are being recklessly employed. One example is the use in medicine of powerful new drugs and treatments before enough about their effects and side-effects is reliably known; and they are no less dangerous because of the enormous debt that modern medicine owes to science.

This is part of a wider tendency which derives from a laboratory outlook: the tendency to treat persons impersonally, as guinea-pigs or as items in a plan. A similar inclination emerges in some social and industrial contexts, when a supposedly scientific approach (though it is not really scientific to treat persons as units, except for purely statistical purposes) is applied to promote efficiency or tidiness without adequate reckoning of the human cost.

Here, too, science is learning from its own mistakes. The aim of the fairly new line of study known as ergonomics is to adapt machines and industrial operations to the needs and convenience of the men who use them, instead of taking the machine or the operation as given, in the style of Procrustes, and requiring the man to adapt himself to it. When one reads of this, and of other instances where science is clearly not being reckless and inhuman, but the reverse, and where, when it *has* been reckless or short-sighted, it shows this commendable readiness to correct itself, one may well be inclined to ask whether any anxieties about 'where science is taking us' are justified. Can we not always rely on science to learn from its errors and to retrieve its mistakes? Is not the remedy for any harmful results of science to be found

[1] 'There is not the slightest doubt that the discoveries of physics *have* frightened mankind, and that there are far too many intelligent people looking askance at science and wondering where it is leading.' From the presidential address by Sir James Gray, F.R.S., at the 1959 meeting of the British Association.

always in more science, not less? And since there always will be more science, for in no field does science ever stand still, is there anything at all to worry about? In any event, too, what other hope is there for the human race except in science progressing and improving itself? What other reliable sources of knowledge and enlightenment are there, outside the scientific realm?

I think there *are* some grounds for anxiety, and also (we will come to this later) some other sources of knowledge; but where dangers are so closely bound up with benefits, the boundary between them, the passing-over point, is often not easy to discern.

For example, it can be argued convincingly that science has helped to make the civilized world a much kinder place by beginning to set men free from cruel religious dogmas, and from the urge to punish that may be stirred by irrational feelings about sin and guilt. This is hardly disputable: the influence of scientific humanism has done a great deal, for instance, to improve the treatment of children and criminals and the insane. But it is also *possible* to treat children too rationally, at the expense of the impulsive affection and even the quick anger they may sometimes need; an entirely rational parent is too remote and godlike for a small child. And again, though the aim of helping criminals to turn away from crime is good and sensible, the subjecting of a man to psychiatry instead of punishment *can* involve a damaging affront to his self-respect, if he is made to feel that he is being treated as laboratory material.

In these fields good and harm are subtly intermingled: which will predominate may often depend largely on what sort of being man is supposed to be.[1] And here, whenever science is applied to human affairs, there is always apt to be present in the background the scientific picture of man as no more than a higher animal, a creature of conditioned reflexes whose spiritual aspirations and religious beliefs (if any) are explicable in terms of fantasies projected from his unconscious mind. And when the scientific picture

[1] This intermingling is particularly close and perilous in the rapidly developing use of drugs and conditioning techniques for treating and influencing mental and emotional states. See William Sargant, *Battle for the Mind*, 1957.

of man is taken over (perhaps not quite consciously but as an underlying assumption) by a society or its rulers, conditions favourable to modern forms of tyranny are likely to arise.

There are some dangers also in the application to human beings and other living organisms of the analytical, dissecting methods on which modern science has grown up. Biologists now recognize that a living organism is not simply an assemblage of parts: it has a wholeness, a *Gestalt*, which is reflected in the relationships between its parts and in its capacity to maintain itself as a continuous entity in spite of unceasing interchange between itself and its environment—

> *It's a very odd thing—*
> *As odd as can be—*
> *That whatever Miss T. eats*
> *Turns into Miss T.*

Even the teeth and bones are in a perpetual state of flux, exchanging substance with the blood, while the blood is in constant intercourse, through the breath and the digestion, with substances from the outer world. It is only because of our particular time-sense, and because 'solid substance' looks and feels solid, that an organism appears to us to be a self-contained permanent structure; it is actually like a fountain with ever-changing water-drops. You cannot hold a fountain still in order to analyse it: it exists in time as well as space and remains a fountain only while it plays.

Modern science, however, has progressed largely by dissection: by breaking down substances and processes into ever-smaller constituents—molecules, atoms, particles, cells, enzymes, genes. A very great deal has been learnt about living organisms by these methods, and much more will be learnt in the future. But they cannot by themselves lead to the complete knowledge that may be had of, say, the working of a watch. For in the functioning of a living organism there is an ever-changing web of relationships, of polarities and interactions and feedbacks, which can never be halted for analysis, nor can the functioning of one element be studied independently of at least some of the rest.

Moreover, the analytical method leads to increasing specialization—to experts knowing more and more about less and less. So one gets a crowd of specialists working on fragments of Humpty Dumpty and nobody who knows how to put him together again.

This specialization is of course necessary and valuable: without it, a detailed knowledge of components could not be obtained. Thus in medicine we need specialists who concentrate on particular diseases or parts of the body; but the tendency of this procedure, if left unbalanced, is to separate diseases from patients and to treat the diseases as entities in their own right. Yet it is probably true that no disease is ever exactly the same in different persons, and certainly true that effective treatment needs to be directed not only at the disease but at the sick person as a whole. Hence we also need non-specialists, general practitioners who can learn from the specialists without losing sight of the patient.

This ideal co-operation between specialists and G.P.s may not be very common, but it is quite practicable and often does occur. In other realms of modern science it hardly can occur: most subjects have become so intricate that only specialists can master them, and many scientific papers are unintelligible outside their own field. Hence there is no such person nowadays as a properly qualified scientific G.P.—no general biologist, say, who would know enough about all the biological specialities to bring them together in his mind and apply them to a living organism as a whole. I don't know whether any man *could* be trained for this exacting task; there is at any rate no course designed for him at present. Thus it often happens that fragments of nature are dealt with by specialists who fail to take full account of how their activities will affect other life-forms, or how the ecological balance may be disturbed.

Specialists, too, are human: a man who is devoting his life to a particular line of research may acquire a proprietary interest in it; nothing else may seem to him to matter quite so much. If he can get results which will add to his knowledge and reputation and prove his power, he may turn a blind eye to the wider repercussions of his doings. This is the kind of attitude which in its many variations makes it appear at times that the aim of science is to 'master' nature—a blunt-instrument procedure, liable to be lethal—instead of learning how to co-operate with her.

These dangers, too, have not gone unrecognized. Ecology is gaining more attention and a higher status among the sciences, and so is the newer ethology, the study of animal behaviour. But these developments have only a limited influence: a different approach to nature by science generally is still needed. Good husbandry in its broadest sense calls for a certain intuitive, almost artistic feeling for what is appropriate and harmonious in the relations of human society to nature and the earth.[1]

Scientists are suspicious of any such advice: it suggests that vague sentiment would replace exact knowledge. I think this suspicion applies no more to the husbandman than to the artist: no more and no less. An artistic approach to anything can degenerate into sentimentality; but a genuine work of art cannot be made merely by learning a technique and taking conscious thought, and this is true (though to a less obvious degree) of human dealings with living creatures and living soil.

For all these reasons I doubt whether more of the same kind of science is the only prescription required for overcoming the dangers and anxieties associated with the present trend and rate of scientific advance. I am not saying that scientific methods should not be used in husbandry or in dealing with social and human problems: they can be valuable in all fields. The point is that the purely scientific, more or less specialized approach needs to be tempered and humanized by a counter-current which expresses different concepts and different values. Where is this counter-current to come from?

[1] This is the feeling that will never be persuaded by economic arguments that hen-batteries and broiler-houses, or broiler-calves, are justified.

CHAPTER XII

Models and Meaning

A counter-current to the purely scientific, analytical approach is something that the old arts culture might be expected to provide, but this is not happening effectively at present. One reason is that the old culture tends to remain on its own side of the gap and has too little contact with science or with scientists. And this is partly because science has undermined so many of its traditions and beliefs; it is no longer sure of itself. Hence, although many of its members find the new culture arid and uncivilized, they feel unable to challenge it, ill-equipped to argue with it on its own ground.

The new scientific culture is an expression of the onlooker-consciousness which began to develop in Western Europe around the end of the fifteenth century. The arts culture has elements which derive from older modes of consciousness, but by now it has been profoundly modified and—almost literally—disheartened by the impact of the new culture during the past few hundred years.

I doubt if enduring bridges can be built between the two levels, the sinking and the rising land. Something could certainly be done, on a modest practical scale, to improve communications between them: to give arts men (including particularly administrators) a better understanding of scientific methods, and to offer young scientists more time and opportunity to sample the stored riches of the old culture, if they wish. But in this context the bridge-building image is too mechanical: a better image might be drawn from the organic realm.

During any epoch there are examples of waxing and waning in cultural life. What always seems desirable, if the best features of the old flowering are not to be quite lost, is that it should pass on some elements which will be taken up into the new growth. Hence I would like to hope that at some future time there will emerge, not a blending of the two existing cultures, but something like a third culture, carrying genes from both parents but with distinctive virtues of its own.

If it were already possible to see in any detail what this third culture would be like, it would not be a new growth when its time came. In any event, our immediate question is whether the scientific culture can develop in such a way as to accept seeds from the old.

This might happen partly through the process whereby science has been led to ask questions about its own methods and findings —questions first asked by Bishop Berkeley in Newton's time, but neglected until they were raised strongly by Mach and Karl Pearson towards the end of the last century.

There is no need here to go into the details of this questioning; it has been extensively written about in recent years.[1] Briefly, what has happened is that scientists, in their efforts to discover 'laws' (or predictive principles) in the phenomena perceived by the senses, have been compelled to go behind the phenomena and to postulate a variety of imperceptible entities—energy, mass, waves, atoms, ions, photons, particles, genes. At first it was supposed that most of these entities were like invisible copies of their visible counterparts—electro-magnetic waves were like the waves that you can send along a piece of rope by moving one end up and down, atoms were like tiny billiard balls, and so on. But it was found that some of them behaved in ways impossible for tangible objects. Hence the tendency now is to treat the imperceptible entities simply as useful concepts, and not to ask 'what' they are, or in what precise sense they can be said to 'exist'. Such questions are regarded as 'metaphysical', outside the range of science.

[1] See Mary Hesse, *Science and the Human Imagination*, 1954, which includes a bibliography.

According to this view, a scientific theory is simply a set of concepts which brings a series of observations into rational order and is considered valid (for the time being) if it successfully *predicts*.[1] It can then be presumed to correspond to some order or pattern in nature, but it does not and need not tell us what the pattern is, so to speak, made of. To ask what matter 'is', is meaningless.

This 'operational' outlook arose first in physics, where most of the imperceptible entities crop up, but it has extended quite widely into other scientific fields. 'Thought-models', or conceptual blueprints, often based on electrical circuits, are used in the study of chemical reactions, in neuro-physiology and in genetics, for example. The thought-model is taken as an illustration of how a natural process *may* work; its validity is judged mainly by whether it yields correct predictions—'If this is right, then under certain conditions the following will be observed.'

Suppose an airman wishes to map a remote stretch of country he has never visited. When he gets over it, he finds that unbroken cloud hides it from his sight. With suitable radar equipment he can produce from echo-soundings a rough map of the country, indicating its main physical features and contours. The map may be of great practical value for navigation (or bomb-dropping), but it will not tell him what the life and people are really like, down there under the cloud.

A good deal of the knowledge gained by modern science about nature is somewhat of this character. It is useful knowledge, predictive knowledge; it gives power—power to control and manipulate nature, to get results that satisfy some human need or desire. Not many scientists, probably, are drawn individually to science by a conscious wish for power. It attracts them primarily because it satisfies other desires: the deep-rooted human desire to create

---

[1] 'The aim of science is to describe the world in orderly language, in such a way that we can if possible foresee the results of those alternative courses of action between which we are always choosing. The kind of order which our description has is purely one of convenience. Our purpose is always to predict.' J. Bronowski, *The Common Sense of Science*, 1951, p. 80.

order out of chaos (often an aesthetic satisfaction), and the elementary impulse of curiosity—the urge to explore, discover, find out.[1] From a social point of view, however, it is the sheer effectiveness of science, the power of its techniques and technology, which ensure its modern prestige. Science is the genie who will change the world and show us how to get anything we want.

But there is one desire that science, in its present form, cannot satisfy: the desire to find *meaning* in the world. Why are we here? Has the universe any purpose that embraces man? Is there any part of man that survives death? To questions such as these science can give no answer; if it tries to do so, it becomes unscientific. Modern philosophers may dismiss such questions as unanswerable and therefore meaningless, but the desire to seek answers to them is as deeply rooted in human nature as are the desires for aesthetic satisfaction or for power.

There is also a simpler sense, less easy to define, in which people want to find meaning in the world. They want to feel at home there, and this depends partly on their relation to their environment—on whether the external scene 'speaks' to them, or appears alien and dumb.

In the Middle Ages, before the epoch of the onlooker-consciousness, it was natural for most people to feel at home in the world in this sense. Their immediate feeling, arising from a consciousness that had not yet acquired the detached onlooker stamp, was reinforced by religious beliefs: the world *was* their home, prepared by God for man. They interpreted nature symbolically, seeing everywhere the signature of spiritual powers.

This kind of meaning had to die out of the world if the onlooker-age of modern science was to come in. Similarly, it was necessary that the answers given to the ultimate questions in the age of faith should cease to be satisfying. They were answers given and accepted on the authority of the Church, and in the onlooker-epoch men have to find authority within themselves.

Hence meaning has been drained both out of the universe and

---

[1] The 'search for truth' is still a potent scientific ideal: the working scientist need not trouble himself with the philosopher's difficulty of defining exactly what 'truth', in this context, signifies.

out of the world of immediate experience. In return, we have modern science, and a scientific culture growing up in the midst of the declining survivals of the old. It is a culture capable of immense achievements, and it is only at the beginning of them. But it is not capable of restoring meaning to the universe or to the world, nor of revealing the 'truth' about them, although it does of course discover many useful 'truths' of an empirical kind. Indeed, one of the functions of modern science—perhaps its fundamental function from a certain point of view—is to bring men to a situation in which they will be driven back on themselves in order to recreate meaning in a world which science has rendered meaningless, and therefore uninhabitable in a full human sense. It is this situation, this null point, that we are approaching today, even while the technology of the scientific culture is going triumphantly ahead with its work of building up around us a man-made environment equipped with the latest conveniences—in themselves not to be despised.

There is a great deal that the scientific culture needs to accomplish in the course of becoming the dominant culture of our epoch. But something else (as I suggested just now) is necessary also: the arising within it of a new impulse which will point towards a third culture—its successor but *not* its antithesis. For the third culture, as I imagine it, will be itself a scientific culture, in a certain sense. It will retain the particular modern virtues of the scientific outlook—disciplined thinking, respect for facts, testing by experiment—but it will use them differently.

At the same time, I believe, it will be (however wildly improbable this sounds) also a religious and an artistic culture. These three elements, essential for any fully human society, were united once: it was inevitable that they should diverge if each was to develop in freedom, but it is necessary that in the future they should come together again as members of an organically differentiated whole. For some impulse towards all three exists in some form, however obscurely, in every human being; he is more or less crippled if any one of them plays no part at all in his conscious life.

CHAPTER XIII

'Magical Feeling'

I have hardly tried yet to answer the question—Where is the counter-current coming from? I don't think it can be answered in specific detail. All I shall attempt in the next section is to look at some ideas which may point towards the counter-current or its tributaries.

First, however, as a kind of interlude, I want to discuss the views of a scientist and an Anglican Christian, Mr. John Wren-Lewis, who in recent years has written extensively on themes closely related to those of this book, and particularly those of the last few chapters. On encountering his essays I felt rather as one might feel on meeting a stranger in some remote foreign clime and hearing him speak English. But then the stranger pulls out a revolver.

I found Mr. Wren-Lewis's language unexpectedly familiar because, first of all, he recognizes that modern science owes its rise to what I have called the emergence of the onlooker-consciousness at the close of the Middle Ages, when the last remnants of the old participating consciousness were dying out and the scientific exploration of the world was free to begin. He also recognizes that one effect of this far-reaching change has been to drain 'meaning' out of the world. He is much concerned, too, with the question of 'where science is taking us', and with the influence of the scientific revolution on the status and prospects of religion and art.

But it soon appears that he is looking at these matters from a point of view diametrically opposed to mine. Or, if 180 degrees

is too strong, let us say 150 degrees. What I have called the emergence of the onlooker consciousness, he calls the 'decline of
magical feeling', and this he regards as pure gain. With equal
enthusiasm he welcomes the draining of 'meaning' from the
world, because—but I am going too fast. It will be fairer to state
his case in a more orderly way.

The great difference between modern scientific civilization and
all preceding civilizations, Mr. Wren-Lewis suggests, lies in this
'decline of magical feeling', by which he means 'the feeling that
the world we meet in experience is not the real world, but only a
veil which people can never know directly except perhaps by
dying'.[1]
In all previous epochs, he believes, feelings of this kind
have played a fundamental part not only in popular religion,
but also in art (largely bent on giving symbolic expression to
realities 'behind the veil'), and in social life, where they led to
acceptance of hierarchical authority (held to derive ultimately
from unseen spiritual powers) and so gave individuals 'a sense
of participating mystically . . . in the great occult body of their
society'.
Hence it does not surprise him that many persons today (he
says) regard the decline of 'magical feeling' as a disaster: they
believe that 'art and social life are completely doomed unless
traditional ways of thinking and feeling can somehow be restored.
For it is being increasingly recognized that most of our social
customs and institutions were evolved in ages when people could

[1] My quotations are all from 'The Decline of Magic in Art and Politics'
(*The Critical Quarterly*, Spring 1960), except where another reference is
given. See also 'The Lure of Pseudo-Science' (*The Twentieth Century*,
February 1959); 'Does Science Show Us a Meaningless Universe?' (*The
Twentieth Century*, September 1959); 'The Vindication of Romance' (*The
Listener*, 1 October 1959); 'Stuff and Science' (*The Listener*, 13 October
1960); and two longer papers, 'The Continuous Fall' (*Hibbert Journal*,
July 1956) and 'Return to the Roots' (Modern Churchmen's Union, 1957).
My study of these essays has left me with great respect for the strong
religious conviction from which Mr. Wren-Lewis evidently writes. I
would ask his pardon if (as is quite likely) I have misunderstood or mis-
represented him in any way.

be relied on to feel organically involved with society to a considerable extent, and are bound to break down in the absence of such
feeling'.

Mr. Wren-Lewis himself, however, is utterly opposed to this
pessimistic point of view. For him, the decline of 'magical
feeling' is 'one of the best things that has ever happened to mankind', on several counts. It has meant 'the liberation of the
human mind from compulsive subservience to mythological
thought-patterns', which should greatly benefit true religion. The
'organic' form of society which it has destroyed was the victim of
an 'organised neurosis' which prevented people from ever really
seeing or meeting each other as persons, but only as 'fellow par-
ticipants in the ritual drama'. And without this decline, the
scientific revolution could hardly have occurred.

Mr. Wren-Lewis is not blind to the 'dangers and horrible
misapplications of modern science', but he insists that the scientific revolution has not brought only material benefits; it is
making a genuine personal life possible at last for millions who
would otherwise be condemned—like their forefathers—to a
mere struggle for existence. And personal relations are for him (as
we shall see shortly) the only basis of true religion.

One reason for discussing these essays is that among writers on
science (or on religion), very few recognize anything like an
evolution of consciousness. Mr. Wren-Lewis does recognize
something like it: thus we can agree that the emergence of the
modern mode of consciousness marks an essential difference between our epoch and its predecessors, and that without it the
scientific revolution could not have occurred. Where we differ
radically is on the status of earlier modes of consciousness.

This disagreement would obviously not matter if no wider
issues were involved. But with his account of 'magical feeling'
Mr. Wren-Lewis is challenging—as he fully recognizes—an influential body of opinion; and quite clearly, if he is right, an
altogether new attitude towards the significance of modern science
and its bearing on religion ought to prevail. He misinterprets
some at least of the writers and thinkers whom he mentions in

this connection;[1] they do not all by any means wish to recover the old 'magical feeling', or to revive earlier forms of social life. It would be quite wrong even to say that they all regret the decline of 'magical feeling'; it is not as simple as that. I would say myself (as I have said already) that the coming of the onlooker-epoch marked a necessary stage in human evolution, and that, like most evolutionary transitions, it can be understood only if it is seen as involving *both* loss and gain—inseparably, the one being the obverse of the other.

But for Mr. Wren-Lewis it is all very simple and clear-cut. 'Magical feeling' was a neurosis which led to fantasy-beliefs, and its decline is sheer gain. Thus he speaks of the decline as 'the beginning of the recovery—or at any rate the partial recovery—of the human race from a universal illness besetting it from the dawn of history'. One naturally wants to know his evidence for this large claim.

The keystone of his whole argument is the Freudian view that 'fantasies about spiritual forces in the occult world are really "projections" or "displacements" of elements in our experience of personal relationships which we seek to avoid recognising'. He insists that 'this is primarily an empirical conclusion, not an opinion to be "refuted" by criticising the philosophical basis of psychoanalytic theory', for Freud's diagnosis was 'based on clinical experience, in which mythological beliefs were actually shown, under analysis, to be symbolic means of escaping from aspects of actual experience which for various reasons people feared to face, and this is still being demonstrated again and again by psychoanalysts'.

A state of consciousness which has been common to most of humanity until quite lately is thus to be regarded as a 'universal illness' on the strength of the findings of a relatively small number of Freudian analysts during recent years (only the Freudians, for analysts of some other schools would interpret the clinical evidence differently).

The Freudian analysts are doubtless fully justified in regarding

[1] They include T. S. Eliot, J. B. Priestley, Jacquetta Hawkes, Kathleen Raine, Owen Barfield, Jung and the Jungians generally, and Rudolf Steiner.

all 'magical feeling' as neurotic, by their standards, and in tracing its origin in their patients to an escape-mechanism. But the *origin* of a belief cannot establish either its truth or its falsity.[1] The real question is whether an 'invisible world' does or does not exist. If it does exist, then it could be that persons who are neurotic by Freudian standards are more likely than 'normal' people to apprehend some token of it. They may be persons who, through some failure to adjust to normal standards, have been shaken out of the conventional beliefs and assumptions which prevail in our epoch. And if after analysis they are free from 'magical feeling', this could mean that they have sunk back comfortably into 'Newton's sleep'.

As to whether an 'invisible world' does or does not exist, one can't be sure exactly what the phrase signifies for Mr. Wren-Lewis. But the existence of *something* behind the scenes—that is, of 'regions' (but not spatial in any ordinary sense) which are apprehended as environment by other forms of consciousness, and where other forms of consciousness are encountered—the testimony for this does not depend simply on 'magical feeling'; nor does the associated belief that the sense-perceptible world is a veil that can be pierced. On both points there is an immense range of testimony—expressed in the most varied and always more or less symbolic language—from the sources of the main religions of East and West and from individual saints and seers and mystics through the ages.

Mr. Wren-Lewis might not disagree entirely with this; for him it is part of the 'universal illness', I suppose. He contends, however, that 'prophetic religion' as distinct from organized religion, and indeed the 'great pioneers of all the major religious traditions',[2] have always been concerned to condemn 'magical feeling' and the beliefs connected with it. This is again a rather large claim, and on the historical evidence it seems a surprising one. It is organized religion which has generally been suspicious

---

[1] Similarly, there is evidence that neurotic conflicts have contributed in some way to the work of many artists, writers and musicians, but the *value* of their work cannot be judged on clinical grounds, as Freud himself recognized.

[2] 'Where is Science taking Us?', *The Student World*, No. 3, 1958.

of anything visionary or mystical, and it is the 'prophets'—individuals speaking from out of their own inspiration or insight —who have borne witness to their experiences of realities 'behind the veil'.

However, Mr. Wren-Lewis has his own interpretation of the prophets, and indeed of the Christian religion.[1] 'Magical feeling', he believes, has perverted religion by leading people to look for God outside their own immediate experience of personal relationships, where alone 'the one true God, who dwells "between man and man", is to be found'.

I think he is right in holding that religion in the future, if it is to retain any potency, will come to derive more and more from personal experience, but not from experience of personal relationships alone. 'Thou shalt love thy neighbour as thyself' is the *second* commandment. The order of the two commandments seems to imply that without a prior love of God there will be something lacking in your personal relationships.[2]

It is hard to tell what 'God' means for Mr. Wren-Lewis, but he clearly regards most conceptions of God as fantasy-products of 'magical feeling':

'The image of God as Father, for example, is in origin not an

[1] And also of William Blake: 'As Blake said, if the salvation of mankind is to come, it can only be through an increase in sensual enjoyment, a cleansing of the doors of perception—not to see another world, but to see this one fully.' Yet Blake wrote: 'I assert for My Self that I do not behold the outward creation & that to me it is hindrance and not action; it is as the dirt upon my feet, No part of Me . . . I question not my Corporeal or Vegetative Eye any more than I would question a Window concerning a Sight. I look thro' it & not at it.'
Of course there have been many conflicting interpretations of Blake; you can read into him almost anything you wish to find there. Still, he seems to me an odd witness for Mr. Wren-Lewis to call.
[2] Mr. Wren-Lewis always renders Luke xvii. 21 as 'The kingdom of God is between you.' The Greek preposition ἐντός can mean either 'within' or 'among', but 'between' seems a shade forced, and not called for by the context. The Pharisees had demanded to know 'when the kingdom of God should come'—i.e. 'when shall we see this kingdom you are always talking about?' Jesus in his reply emphasizes simply that the kingdom is not something that can be seen, but a state of being that has to be inwardly experienced. His words do not suggest that the kingdom can arise *only* 'between man and man'.

attempt to ascribe fatherliness to an imagined Master Mind behind the scenes of nature, but rather a direct expression of an
experienced truth about the creative power of love . . . The image
of Creation expresses the experience that the forms of physical
life can be determined by the activity of love in personal life,
rather than *vice versa*; and the image of Heaven expresses the
hope that all existence may be transformed into the service of
creative love.'

One might be inclined to regard Mr. Wren-Lewis as an extreme
anti-pantheist, but I believe this would be misleading. For although he writes, 'It is utterly impossible to base religious belief
of any sort upon the idea of order or pattern in the natural
world', he also writes in the same essay,[1] 'The idea of the world
as first and foremost a system of material objects in space and
time is an abstraction from what we really know, and when the
great religions describe mankind as *fallen into illusion*, it is because
men and women everywhere have come, for most of their lives,
to mistake this abstraction for reality itself.'

Here perhaps we arrive at a fundamental reason for Mr. Wren-
Lewis's rooted objection to 'magical feeling'. He seems to
assume that when 'magical feeling' gives an inkling of an 'invisible world' behind the veil, the reference is to another world
not entirely unlike our own—a world of objects and entities and
apparently self-contained personalities; a 'spirit-land' or even a
kind of 'fairy-land'; a hidden world in which strange things happen 'by magic', but still a world in which subjects are still subjects and objects, objects. Now it is true that people can be quite
easily led by 'magical feeling' to form notions of this kind of what
lies 'behind the veil' (or 'across the threshold'), and they may
have dreamlike experiences which seem to support such notions;
but this means only that they are not equipped to interpret their
experiences.

By those who are so equipped it is repeatedly emphasized that
nothing beyond the veil can be accurately described in human
language; yet human language has to be used.

[1] 'Does Science Show Us a Meaningless Universe?' (*The Twentieth
Century*, September 1959).

Why not keep silence, or use only the symbolic language of art? I think this depends on the sort of idolatry which is most likely to hold sway during a particular period of evolution. In our epoch the commonest, well-nigh universal form of idolatry is that of taking the material space-time world as a final reality; hence it may be necessary to insist that other orders of reality exist 'behind the veil', even though any account of them is liable to be taken literally, in which case *they* will become idols in their turn. To give an obvious and rather crude example, if 'Heaven' is taken to be a 'place' where persons in white robes play harps, this is idolatry. But to say that nothing can be known about a state of being called 'Heaven' except through the experience of human relationships—or that 'Heaven' *is* simply (or is entirely created by) such experience—that is to go to another and equally dangerous, all-too-human extreme.

When the 'great religions' call it an illusion to mistake for reality 'the idea of the world as first and foremost a system of material objects in space and time', they are giving warning against one form of idolatry (not peculiar to our epoch but much stronger today than ever before). But they also say or indicate something else. They say that there can be a μετάνοια, or change of consciousness, whereby the veil is penetrated because something (not everything) of what lies behind it comes within the range of conscious experience.

Mr. Wren-Lewis will have none of this, because presumably it is too suggestive of 'magical feeling'. But a further reason for his general attitude—I would tentatively think, for it may well be that I have not fully understood it—is that he does not appear to recognize a real *evolution* of consciousness. He does recognize that the perceived outer world and the beliefs held about it reflect a prevailing mode of consciousness; but his picture is of one vast epoch dominated by 'magical feeling'—the 'universal illness' which has beset mankind 'from the dawn of history'—followed at last by our own epoch, when we are beginning to be cured.

This means (in the language I would use) that he is both looking at the world and discussing all these difficult questions from the standpoint of the onlooker-consciousness, and taking this to be the only valid, the only healthy, standpoint. And from this standpoint it may be true that the experience of personal relationships is almost the only remaining way in which the Divine can be apprehended in the world.[1] To the pure onlooker-consciousness the first commandment of Christ makes no sense; but the second still can be, at least partially, understood, and, though far from easily, obeyed.

The onlooker-epoch is a necessary stage in human history; hence I would agree that the 'decline of magical feeling' has also been necessary, and that any nostalgia for it, or any attempts to recover it in its old form, are misguided. And I would agree also (as I have already emphasized) that the rise of modern science is both necessary and potentially beneficial (and not only in some obvious fields, medicine or domestic convenience, where on the whole it has been very beneficial already). But it seems to me that the welcome given by Mr. Wren-Lewis to modern science and technology is too uncritical, as for example when he writes:

'Perhaps the most remarkable feature of our modern world is the fact that romantic feelings about the significance of personal life are no longer accompanied by a sense that the physical world must be denied, as they have been in most ages, for the simple reason that we take it for granted that the physical world can and should be manipulated to express our visions of beauty, justice and love in human relationships.'

There can be no quarrel with this ideal, but neither the 'manipulations' of the world most in evidence, nor the motives behind them, seem to be quite living up to it at present.

Mr. Wren-Lewis wants to make the world free for science, unimpeded by 'magical feeling', to improve; but I think he does not appreciate what is likely to happen if the only religious check on scientific aims and values is to come from the experience of personal relationships, and if no kind of religious awareness is to be had from experience of the perceived outer world. This is

[1] This is perhaps partly why the early stages of the onlooker-epoch have been marked by a peculiarly insensitive and rapacious treatment of the earth, and also (in spite of wars and atrocities) by a great advance in the humane treatment of and care for people. The Welfare State in its various aspects, more and less sympathetic, belongs to the onlooker-age.

what I meant just now by 'all-too-human'. If human persons are to be solely responsible, through their relationships with other persons, for whatever effective religion exists, there is not likely to be very much of it—not nearly enough to control the power-drives which enter into the pursuit of science and technology.

Moreover, as Mr. C. S. Lewis has noted,[1] the idea of gaining power over nature can be very deceptive: it is apt to mean that some men (those in control of the scientific tools) gain increased power over other *men*; this will not tend to improve the quality of personal relationships, but the reverse. What Mr. Wren-Lewis recommends as the only true religion would have the effect of handing over the physical world to science; in practice, to men for whom power and adventure and discovery are more important than any 'visions of beauty, justice and love in human relationships'.

When Mr. Wren-Lewis is writing about the physical world, he seems not to distinguish clearly between the world as described by science and the world we directly perceive through the senses. When for instance he says that 'it is utterly impossible to base religious belief of any sort upon the idea of order or pattern in the natural world', this is true of the world described by science; as he himself says in several places, *that* world is 'meaningless'. But the world perceived by the senses need not be meaningless. To the pure onlooker-consciousness it *is* meaningless; but that is because this mode of consciousness is limited and specialized. Here again, it seems to me, Mr. Wren-Lewis is writing from the special standpoint of the onlooker-consciousness and treating it as final; a condition of healthful clarity at last and permanently achieved.

Nevertheless, when Mr. Wren-Lewis speaks of finding no evidence of the Divine in the outer universe and looks to personal relationships as the one source of authentic religion in the future, it is to me as though he had read something true and prescient in a foreign language and had translated it incorrectly. I will try to explain this later on.

[1] *The Abolition of Man*, 1943.

CHAPTER XIV

Dangerous Knowledge

N ow we will return to the question—Where is the 'counter-current' to come from? So far I have used the phrase rather vaguely; I mean by it two things:

1. A humanizing influence which would correct the tendencies of science to subordinate human values to technological ends, and to lose sight of the whole human being because of the inevitability of specialization.

2. An influence which might extend the resources of knowledge available for guiding and illuminating research.

With the first influence we are on familiar ground: this is what the old arts culture ought to supply and to some extent still does. But it is gradually losing its claim to do so with authority. This is partly because it is felt not to have enough accurate knowledge for answering the questions, social or human, that arise in the context of the modern world. The tendency is to turn for answers to science—not generally to scientists themselves (who are too busy), but to professional experts in the relevant fields, or to some more or less scientific method of inquiry intended to 'get at the facts'.

This procedure is very often fully justified and should probably be extended: decisions on social policy are still apt to be taken without adequate knowledge of the facts. But the effect is both to restrict the influence of the old culture and to reinforce the belief (already fairly widespread) that it speaks only a vague language of idealism and exhortation, not based on solid evidence and out of touch with modern needs. We hear sometimes, for example, of a revival of religion, but generally this means chiefly that under the stresses of modern life more people are turning to a Church for private comfort. It does not mean that religion is regaining its old authority as an inspired source of guidance on questions of value and as final arbiter on questions of right and wrong.

This situation reflects the fact that both cultures today are under the sign of the onlooker-consciousness. But whereas the coming in of this modern mode of consciousness has created the new culture and set it on a rising wave, the effect on the old culture has been to impoverish it and to deprive it of light.

This brings us to the second of the two influences mentioned above, and here we are on much less familiar ground. I think we need, and shall need increasingly in the future, new sources of knowledge both for illuminating science directly and for regenerating the old culture, so that it may speak once more with authority in its own fields and also become an effective critic of scientific excess.

This idea is unfamiliar because in our epoch we are inclined to assume that the only reliable ways of gaining *knowledge* are already possessed by science and by science alone. What need or possibility is there of other ways?

But is it certain that modern science possesses knowledge fully adequate even for its own guidance, let alone for offering guidance in other realms, or that it has the means to extend its knowledge adequately in all necessary directions? To me it often appears that scientists are like miners sinking shafts in volcanic regions, or like engineers experimenting with the controls of a powerful machine, not built by themselves, and most of it hidden behind a barrier which their tools cannot breach.

Some scientists might not entirely disagree: they do feel that they have only a limited understanding of the energies they handle or of the reactions they set up, whether in the interior of matter, in the subtle process of the human body or in the depths of the human mind. But even those who feel this are usually fairly confident that by existing methods of research they will in time obtain all the necessary knowledge—if nothing disastrous intervenes.

I am of course not questioning the potency and austere virtue of these methods, nor suggesting that a counter-current could offer science a more effective way of obtaining its own particular form of power-giving knowledge about the world. The question is whether this kind of knowledge is adequate for coping with the powers and perils which science itself has brought into modern life; and, if not, whether other ways of obtaining authentic knowledge, with some relevance to science, are or ever have been available.

Any such notion is likely to be suspect for at least two reasons:

1. Because of the well-known fact that science began its modern advance only when it concentrated on observation and experiment and confined itself to questions which could be answered in those terms—questions concerned with *how* things behave, not with *why* they behave as they do or with *what* they are. Any idea that other ways of gaining knowledge might be applicable to the scientific field will suggest the contamination of the true scientific method with some of those alien considerations which science has resolutely discarded.[1]

2. Because of the equally well-known fact that a vast amount of supposed knowledge about nature and the world, widely accepted as authentic in the past, has been shown to be false. Indeed, anyone who examines the strange medley of traditional lore and travellers' tales which went into the medieval picture of the world may well be inclined to brush away all pre-scientific knowledge of the world as a rag-bag of superstitions and to thank Heaven we have escaped from it—why, Newton might have *been* an alchemist if he had lived in the Middle Ages! But medieval knowledge of nature had come a long way from its primary sources; it was confused and fading in the twilight of an epoch. If one looks back widely through time and space over the major civilizations of the past, it seems to me parochial to suppose that they

---

[1] 'The great achievement of the scientific revolution was that men gradually and painfully learned to recognize that aesthetic and existential considerations were simply not relevant to answering questions about how things behave and how they can be manipulated.' J. Wren-Lewis, 'Where is Science Taking Us?', op. cit.

had access to *no* genuine knowledge about nature, and rash to take it for granted that the only way of access to such knowledge is by the methods of modern science.

Nowadays we assume that all the reliable knowledge about nature and the world is such that it can be acquired by anyone with the necessary ability who spends enough time on it. In early epochs it was held that certain forms of knowledge, with a very definite bearing on the human situation and on man's dealings with his environment, could be acquired only by someone who was prepared to work at changing *himself*. This was the basis of initiation, and of the numerous myths of the hero who has to undergo some ordeal, or to undertake a perilous journey, in order to lay hold of a treasure. The essential outcome was not that the knowledge was then told to him, or that he was given secret books to read (though sometimes he probably was), but that his inner eyes were opened and he acquired the knowledge by experiencing it.

Hence the Mysteries were guarded not only because anyone who broke into them unprepared might misuse whatever fragments of esoteric knowledge he could grasp, and not only because the priests wanted to enhance their power by keeping such knowledge to themselves (though no doubt this motive sometimes came in), but also because this kind of knowledge was found to have a dangerous quality: it could shatter anyone not trained and ready for it.[1]

Early initiations were perhaps carried out almost always under priestly direction, generally requiring the candidate to spend three days in a trance-like condition not far removed from death; but the essence of initiation is an inward process which can be accomplished with no outward ritual, though it may always involve something like death and rebirth.

This conception of dangerous knowledge need not seem very far-fetched. In writings on initiation there are frequent references

[1] Esoteric knowledge is now called 'classified' knowledge. Anyone who gets hold of it without being entitled to it will be in danger.

to 'crossing the threshold' as the point where particular dangers arise. It is the point of transition from the world of ordinary experience to a realm where many values are reversed, and where the candidate becomes more or less suddenly aware of hidden and dark elements in himself. Sometimes it is said that at this point he meets his 'Double', or 'shadow-self'—a profoundly disturbing experience. We hear also of a 'guardian of the threshold', who gives warning of the dangers and may turn back candidates who are not prepared.

In all this there are obvious resemblances to the terminology which has arisen (apparently independently) in modern psychology. Between the conscious and unconscious regions of the psyche lies a 'threshold'; we hear of a 'censor' who prevents the conscious mind from getting to know too much about the unconscious, and (in Jungian terms) of the 'shadow'—the 'inferior being in ourselves, the one who wants to do all the things that we do not allow ourselves to do, who is everything that we are not, the Mr. Hyde to our Dr. Jekyll'.[1]

There are, too, well-recognized dangers in 'crossing the threshold'—that is, in consciously encountering the dynamic emotional elements which reside below it. Indeed, certain forms of insanity seem to result precisely from an upsurging of unconscious elements which the conscious ego is unable to control. The accusing voices which a mentally ill person may hear, and may attribute to some external conspiracy, come in fact from beyond the threshold, his own.

I am not suggesting that 'crossing the threshold' in initiation, and 'crossing the threshold' in the sense of modern psychology, are the same. Perhaps there is need for a modern way of initiation, and it may be because this need is not recognized—because indeed the very idea of initiation has come to be generally associated with pre-scientific mumbo-jumbo—that psychiatric methods of penetrating the threshold are in such demand. Or it may be that because of the unbearable dryness of the island of modern consciousness, there has arisen a craving both to explore and to let in the sea. But the immediate point I want to make is simply

[1] Frieda Fordham, *An Introduction to Jung's Psychology* (Pelican), 1953.

that the idea of 'perilous knowledge' is not an archaic fantasy; modern psychiatry has confirmed it.[1]

In the search for this kind of knowledge there are two paths, that of the mystic and that of the occultist, so called. They merge into one another but can be distinguished; sometimes they may even seem to be opposed.

The mystic is seeking for knowledge of God: his experience may give him this, as a personal inner conviction, but generally he will not be able to put the heart of his experience into words. He may describe the stages of his path, and he may try to convey in words something of his final experience, but it will not be communicable to others, except partially and indirectly, through inadequate metaphors, or negatively, by saying what it is not.

The occultist is also seeking knowledge of God, but in and through His works. The pure mystic tends to regard everything manifest as *maya*, illusion, and thus seeks to free himself from its toils in his endeavour to lose (or find) himself in the Light behind the light. The occultist wishes to know *how* God is manifest in His creation; to understand the processes of becoming and passing away, the polaric relation between potency and appearance (for example, between a seed and a flower in full bloom). He endeavours to cross the threshold with his eyes open and to observe how the realm of appearance is brought into existence and sustained.

An occultist is inclined to regard a mystic as one who is content with a transcendent experience which, precisely because it transcends rational criteria, may deceive him as to its true character, and is in any event of value mainly to himself. A mystic is inclined to regard an occultist as one who, in seeking knowledge, fetters himself to the realm of inessentials and loses the pearl of great price.

These contrasting criticisms can both be justified, in some cases. If a mystic is concerned only with a flight 'alone to the

[1] Compare (at several removes) the conclusion of Fred Hoyle's novel *The Black Cloud*, 1957, where high-voltage knowledge causes two deaths.

alone' and regards the creation as dross, he will at best gain knowledge of only one aspect of the Divine, and he may be subject to illusions arising on a higher level from the egoism he believes he has cast off. If an occultist seeks for knowledge as a means of personal power, egoism is likely to make him into some kind of magician; he will then have turned away from God and may find himself dealing with agencies opposed to the Divine.

But these are extreme cases, in which the temptations characteristic of the two paths have not been overcome. It may be that in early periods the two paths were necessarily separate, but in the Christian era I think this is no longer so. When the devotional and the sacramental are united, the two paths meet.

Still, there is always a possibility of divergence, even of conflict. Perhaps one can see in the distinction between the two paths, one leading towards realms of inner experience, away from the world, the other towards deeper knowledge of the world, a foreshadowing of the gap between the two cultures at the present time.

It is the knowledge sought by the occultist, rather than the more inward experiences of the mystic, which could be relevant to modern scientific research. But 'occultist' and 'occultism' are words I dislike; it might be preferable to make them applicable only to the past. Not only are they disagreeable to most modern ears, but they are positively misleading in certain respects. Their etymology suggests the cultivation of some kind of hidden knowledge, the preserve of secret societies with strictly guarded admission rites. This may have been generally true of occultism in the time of the Mysteries, but such procedures are unsuited both to modern social conditions and to the stage in the evolution of consciousness that has been reached today. We must banish these associations in approaching the question of the next stage in the evolution of consciousness—a question bound up with the possibility of a 'third culture' arising in the future.

CHAPTER XV

Beyond the Map

In an earlier chapter it was suggested that the normal consciousness of today could be regarded as lying somewhere between two extremes—one in which the world appears illuminated and one in which it looks like mechanical scenery.[1] This second mode may indicate what could happen if the onlooker-consciousness were to evolve still further along the same narrowing path that has led down to it. If the second mode became normal, a world of drably mechanical scenery could become the accepted natural world.

Philosophers might then read the nature poetry of our own epoch and look at its paintings and conclude that those old writers and artists had been projecting unconscious fantasies on to the outer scene, for it was obvious that their romantic descriptions had no real counterpart in nature. Perhaps there would be a few rebels, in line of descent from D. H. Lawrence, who would argue that the old poets and painters had been right, had known how to *see*; but these dissidents would soon be silenced in the name of scientific realism.

In any event, a further evolution of consciousness towards the depressive mode is not something to be welcomed. We need to look for other directions of change.

I have already discussed briefly some of the evidence which indicates that the focus of consciousness can be induced to vary over a wide range. There is the evidence from drugs, and the much more important and far-reaching evidence from the reports

[1] See Chapter V.

of mystical and psychical experience.[1] These are so extensive and varied that they can only be touched on here. I want to mention a particular type of experience, uncommon but well attested, because of its bearing on the familiar assumption that all these experiences are purely subjective and can tell us nothing about the character of the world. I mean those 'out-of-the-body' experiences which are consciously recognized as such.

This sometimes happens as the result of a sudden shock or danger, when death seems imminent, or it may happen at a critical stage in a severe illness, or occasionally under an anaesthetic. There are also much rarer records of extended out-of-the-body experiences, when the person feels himself to be living in some other kind of body or vehicle, and able to move about in a space which is not physical space but may appear to interpenetrate physical space, while having a 'geometry' of its own.[2]

These experiences can be explained away as dreams, but the persons concerned also have ordinary dreams, and their report is that no one who has an out-of-the-body experience, and recognizes it as such, is likely to confuse it with dreaming. According to the rarer reports, too, it is not difficult during an extended out-of-the-body experience to tell when dream or fantasy elements intrude into it, as they sometimes may.

Most people will still be inclined to dismiss the whole thing as fantasy or hallucination; but perhaps they are looking at it the wrong way round. The question to ask may not be, 'How can consciousness exist outside the body?' but 'How can human consciousness maintain itself in the body?' *That* may be the miracle which it has taken aeons of evolution to bring about. Even now, human consciousness in the body is precarious; a small shock or

[1] The distinction between 'psychical' and 'mystical' is important, but perhaps not quite so absolute as is sometimes assumed. It may depend partly on the 'quality' and intention of the experience, rather than on whatever 'environment' this may seem to have.

[2] See Dr. J. H. M. Whiteman, *The Mystical Life* (Faber, 1961); Dr. Robert Crookall, *The Study and Practice of Astral Projection* (Aquarian Press, 1961); also 'A Voice from the Grandstand', by Auckland Geddes (Baron Geddes), *Edinburgh Medical Journal*, June 1937.

a slight disturbance of the delicate chemical balance in the blood is enough to make it dark. But the fact that consciousness cannot keep alight within an injured body is not a proof that consciousness outside the body is impossible. Draw the blinds at midday and you darken a room, but not the sun. The rare persons who have reported coherently on out-of-the-body experiences find their consciousness enhanced.

Mystical and psychical experiences are not amenable to ordinary methods of scientific investigation, but they can be studied in a scientific spirit by persons to whom they come (though this has not been common hitherto), and they can be approached in a scientific spirit by anyone who wants to know more about them. This should mean a study of the records—not a brief or easy task—and then a willingness to suspend judgment on issues which science can neither prove nor disprove.

A convenient way (which sounds quite scientific) of putting all these issues safely aside is to say: 'Yes, some mystical experiences are doubtless genuine—not invented and not pathological. Science cannot yet explain how they arise or why they carry such peculiar conviction. They may have something to do with bringing the rhythms of the brain into tune with some fundamental frequencies in nature: perhaps they give direct access to the kind of experience which can also be had through the medium of music. They obviously bring great satisfaction and happiness to individuals: it would be useful if we could learn how to induce them by some harmless drug or fairly simple technique.'

This is the assumption already mentioned: that all such experiences are bound to be wholly subjective and can have no bearing on the outer world. But it is also possible—though unprovable by scientific means—that they sometimes explore worlds, or realms of being, which are just as real as the everyday world but are not disclosed to ordinary perceptions.

'Possible, I suppose, but not very probable,' a sceptical scientist might reply. 'In any event, we have still a vast amount to learn about *this* world, and whatever we learn is likely to be useful in some way, sooner or later. Why should we trouble about vague speculations that cannot be put to any kind of test? Let the mystics enjoy their experiences by all means, but don't expect science to spend time on them.'

How one estimates probabilities in this kind of field may depend largely on temperament. To me the universe appears so unfathomably rich and mysterious that the existence in it of no realms of being other than the physical-perceptible seems improbable. Moreover, we don't even know what the physical world *is*; we know only the 'display' given to our senses. I can readily suppose that there are worlds within worlds, depth upon depth; perhaps as many worlds as are needed to reflect all possible states of consciousness.

As regards the objection that science has enough to do in studying the ordinary world, this is rather as though meteorologists were to say: 'We have enough to do in studying the atmosphere up to the level of the highest mountain-top, about five miles: that is an obvious natural limit set by the contours of the earth. Time enough to think of higher levels when we have learnt all we can about the lower ones.' In fact, meteorologists find that in order to study realistically the climate of the earth, they need to explore as high as they can go—even beyond the atmosphere into outer space—and to reckon with radiations from the sun. One might wish that a very small fraction of the enthusiastic attention which science is now devoting to exploring these outer regions could be given to studying the records of journeys into realms beyond the frontier of normal consciousness. For these realms are not remote from our own (much less remote than the moon is from the earth), and knowledge of them, I believe, will eventually prove to be necessary for understanding even the physical world, and still more the world of living organisms.

I do not mean that these realms can be opened up by scientific methods; entry into them cannot be forced. But it does not seem excessive to ask of science that it should not dismiss offhand as fantasy what the explorers have to say.

However, these far-reaching journeys are for the few; they show how limited ordinary consciousness (and hence the ordinary picture of the universe) is, but they are too rare to indicate what the next stage in the general evolution of consciousness should be, if we are to move towards a third culture which will retain the hard-won scientific virtues but will overcome the dangers that arise from driving fast along the technological highway in the darkness of the onlooker-age.

I will call the next stage the 'new imagination', because I think that in order to gain some idea of its character we must link it on to the imaginative approach to nature which came to promising expression at the time of the Romantic Revival, in reaction against 'Newton's sleep', but faded out under the smoke-pall of nineteenth-century industrialism.

The scientific virtues depend on clear thinking and conscious control, and even on something which might seem antagonistic to any form of imaginative participation in the world—on being able to retain a certain detachment from nature. Hence the 'new imagination' must not be accompanied by any blurring of consciousness, any sinking into a vague, dreamlike state. The way towards it will not lie through what is usually meant by 'psychic development', whereby a deliberate endeavour is made to cultivate psychic faculties, such as clairvoyance or mediumship, for their own sake.

But to draw the right distinctions here is not always easy—for what is 'clairvoyance'? It is perhaps generally taken to signify a kind of inner sight which discloses certain normally invisible aspects of the world. If it is regarded as a special psychic faculty, quite distinct from ordinary thinking, then it should probably rank as a gift which belongs to the past—to an earlier stage in the evolution of consciousness. This kind of clairvoyance had to die out if the onlooker-consciousness, essential for the development of modern science, was to come in.

But clairvoyance can also be regarded as beginning with a heightened state of consciousness akin to imaginative apprehension. The poet and the artist are not aware of cultivating a special psychic faculty—they would usually recoil from any thought of doing so—yet one might say that by normal standards they are clairvoyant in the sense of perceiving more in the world than most of us do; and if we respond to their work we are made temporarily capable of sharing, to some degree, in their experience. Or, if we are ourselves able to look at the world with imagination, we are looking at it in this same kind of way; the difference is that probably we see less and are unable to render what we see in a communicable form.

Experiences of this kind, whether elicited by a work of art or by the outer world directly, have two characteristics: we feel that we are no longer quite apart from the scene but are drawn into a kind of sympathy or communion with it, and the scene appears to have an enhanced meaning; indeed, we may feel that we are now seeing its 'real' aspect for the first time.

All such experiences can be attributed to a projection of unconscious contents on to the outer world: the enhanced meaning we assign to the scene is then explained as being simply part of ourselves. Probably there is some truth in this theory, but as usually presented it seems to me misleading. It assumes that there is a kind of independently existing neutral screen (nature as normally perceived), which is waiting out there for the unconscious to project an emotional colour upon it. But the world we normally perceive is not simply 'out there', a panorama independent of the perceiving mind. If nature presents roughly the same appearance to most people—which cannot be proved but may be reasonably assumed—this is because there is a normal average level of consciousness. If the level changes, the perceived world changes also: for a heightened consciousness, it has enhanced meaning. But this is no more (or no less) a projection than is the ordinary appearance of the world.

One might say that projection occurs in both cases, but I doubt if 'projection' is the right word. Somehow the unconscious mind of the perceiver co-operates always in producing the display—how, we do not know. To me it seems preferable to regard the display as a form of symbolic language in which we can read more or less meaning according to our capacity for response. Unless the inner eye is open, the outer eye sees only one aspect of the creation, the finished work.[1]

*

[1] 'There can suddenly be opened within the heart or in the mind a

It is not necessary to speak here of how higher levels of consciousness can be attained; nor am I qualified to do so. It is for the explorers themselves to speak.[1] But a few words may perhaps be added about the relation of conscious to unconscious in this particular connection.

A simple formula is to draw a sharp distinction between the unconscious and the 'super-conscious', but this is too facile. On the way to higher states of consciousness, the unconscious is not simply ignored and left behind.[2] There is (as we saw in Chapter XIV) a 'threshold' to be crossed and a fear of crossing it to be overcome; and it is the same with endeavours to explore the unconscious.[3] *How* the threshold is crossed—with what preparation and with what aims—may make all the difference. Perhaps one might even say that the super-conscious is the unconscious transformed—transformed by being brought into the light of consciousness and integrated with the conscious centre.

There was a time in human history when conscious apprehension embraced more of the unconscious than it does now; the

realm of experience that is not the external world (though it may interpenetrate it) and we are then bathed in the *light of meaning*—in that light without violence, which is pure experience, luminosity without shadow, in which the hardness of self vanishes. . . . Every experience of that light deeply creates us. It is creating light, transforming meaning, which all have sought since the beginning of time, light that can do no violence to anyone, meaning that shows us what we have always known and never had the strength to remember.' Maurice Nicoll, *The Mark*, 1954, p. 20.

[1] See, e.g., Rudolf Steiner's *Knowledge of Higher Worlds*, and other works.

[2] 'In creative experience a true ascent necessarily involves at the same time a true descent. Each is an exact measure of the other. We are not at one with heaven until we are also perfectly reconciled to hell, and the ancient war between them in our souls and the soul of man is over.' H. I'A. Fausset, *The Flame and the Light*, 1958, p. 33.

[3] 'These fears are not found only among persons who are frightened by the pictures Freud painted of the unconscious; they also troubled the originator of psychoanalysis himself, who confessed to me that it was necessary to make a dogma of his sexual theory because this was the sole bulwark of reason against a possible "outburst of the black flood of occultism". In these words Freud was expressing his conviction that the unconscious still harboured many things that might lend themselves to "occult" investigations, as is in fact the case.' C. G. Jung, *The Undiscovered Self*, 1958, pp. 48–9.

threshold was more permeable; the conscious island was not sharply separated from the sea. Now we have made it separate; we suffer from dryness, from lack of contact with the life-giving mother-ocean; and we are always under a temptation to plunge back into the sea. Something like this is what happens in mediumship and uncontrolled psychism. The higher states of consciousness are different from this; the waters are drawn up by the sun and rain falls on the dry land.

CHAPTER XVI

Nature's Language

Present-day science (we have seen) has gained power over the material world by going behind the phenomena and forming concepts—thought-models and theories—which correspond in some way to the patterns of nature's workings. The price of this highly effective method is that the world as directly experienced by the senses is left aside. In applied science and technology there is of course a return to the sense-perceptible world, but in order to manipulate it; and if your aim is to manipulate nature, you will be inhibited from fully experiencing nature, for this requires a different—a non-violent and in some degree an aesthetic—approach.

There are some exceptions to this trend, most notably in the 'natural history' fields. Here the recent tendency has been for scientists to leave their laboratories and to devote themselves to wonderfully patient observation of how living creatures naturally behave, and of the intimate and intricate relationships between their lives and their environments. The phenomena themselves are thus the teachers, and for what they teach an old-fashioned phrase, 'the wisdom of nature', may still be appropriate. Here, perhaps, we can see an indication of one way in which a different kind of science could develop alongside the analytical science of today.

If one pictures in the mind's eye, as clearly and vividly as one can, the growth of a flower from seed to blossom and back again to seed, picturing and noting (as Goethe did) its rhythm of alternating expansion and contraction,[1] one has learnt something about its character and behaviour—its 'gesture'—which one will not learn from analytical or taxonomic botany, essential as these lines of study also are. The two approaches, the analytical and the pictorial re-creating, are not opposed but complementary. Or one can try to distinguish and re-create in the mind's eye the particular gesture of a bird or animal—the bird with its quick, darting, nervous attention to its surroundings, very different from the watchful but withdrawn behaviour of a cat, and still more different from the static, ruminative behaviour of a cow. The bird seems to live in its nerves and senses, the cow in its digestive system.

This way of looking at living things is of course not at all original; something like it has always come naturally to many people, especially to artists, but not only to them. It is quite different from the sentimental way of projecting human feelings on to nature, of personalizing animals and so on; in fact, the very opposite of it. Scientists rightly dislike this anthropomorphic approach, not only because it is misleading, a positive obstacle to exact knowledge, but also because it is messy—a pouring of human emotion over nature like a sticky syrup.

From the scientific way of studying natural processes and animal habits with objective detachment, in order to learn about them as they are, a very great deal has been gained, and not only in strictly scientific terms. Very many people have come to enjoy nature in this way: the popularity of bird-watching is one example. But 'detachment' is not quite the right word for this attitude, although a preliminary detachment is necessary. Anyone who stops at detachment is liable to regard nature merely as something to be used or profited from, and that is where the mistreatment of nature and the earth begins. Detachment should lead on to imaginative insight, an endeavour to enter into natural processes with sympathy, even with affection, but without humanizing them.

[1] Expansion from the seed into leaves and leaf-bearing shoots; contraction into the calyx; expansion into the blossom; contraction into pistils and stamens; expansion of ovary into fruit; contraction into seed.

The re-creation of a 'gesture' before the mind's eye, however, is more of a deliberate exercise: what is the point of it? By itself it can hardly yield any immediate new knowledge of nature in the modern scientific sense, but I think it can have value on several levels.

On the simplest level it does lead to a certain kind of knowledge, or rather it enhances the knowledge gained by simply looking at living things with imaginative sympathy. This kind of knowledge is personal, subjective, hardly communicable; it gives rise to nothing measurable and to no testable predictions, and it is not a means of obtaining more power over nature. But the more strictly scientific knowledge we get, the more necessary is it, I would say, to cultivate imaginative knowledge as a counter-current. In pursuing analytical knowledge we stand apart from the world of nature and use it as a field for dissection and experiment; in imaginative knowledge we live into nature and enrich our experience with hers. If only analytical knowledge is cultivated, the years of our life become a dry season.

On another level, I believe, the exercise of re-creating the growing forms and gestures of living things can lead us to knowledge that may have scientific value: a knowledge of formative processes that could be complementary to the analytical knowledge of unit parts. By following imaginatively, but in accurate detail, the growth or gesture of a living thing, one is approaching an apprehension of its *Gestalt*, the 'wholeness' which gives it its typical character. This was Goethe's approach: a few aspects of it are all I can mention here.[1]

Goethe's aim was to let natural phenomena speak to him. He held that by immersing oneself in the phenomena, and by relating and comparing them, one could 'learn to think creatively in the wake of nature'. This means more than merely contemplating and enjoying natural phenomena, as perceived by the ordinary senses. Goethe, too, sought to 'go behind the phenomena', as a modern scientist does, but in a different way.

The modern way is to form a mental model of a causal structure

[1] For a full account and discussion, see Ernst Lehrs, *Man or Matter* (second edition, 1958), op. cit.

lying behind the phenomena; if your model is correct, it will add to your powers of prediction and control. You turn away from experience of the phenomena for the sake of increased power. The Goethean way is not to impose a theory of your own on the phenomena, but to aim at deepening your experience of them until they themselves begin to disclose something of their origin, their 'becoming'.[1]

If you take the first way, the particular part of nature you are dealing with is deprived of meaning: it *has* to be, in order that you may be free to manipulate it for your own purposes. If you take the second way, the phenomena acquire an enhanced meaning the further you penetrate into them with your consciousness.[2]

I will not discuss Goethe's views on the 'primal phenomenon' (*Urphänomen*), or on 'type' and 'archetype', but I would like to add a few words on his celebrated 'archetypal plant' (*Urpflanze*), for this seems to be often misunderstood.

He quite clearly did *not* mean a primeval ancestral plant which had once lived on the earth; nor did he mean a mere mental concept or image. We must imagine the *Urpflanze* as a creative agency which does not itself enter into visible manifestation, but gives rise—as though from a perpetual fountain—to all the manifested varieties of the plant world.

To the onlooker-consciousness, the notion of an archetypal plant actually existing, not merely as an idea but as a creatively potent entity, must seem sheer fantasy—what evidence for it could there be? Well, if a modern scientist wants to gain knowledge of something he cannot directly perceive, what does he do? He has recourse to a scientific instrument, which serves in some way to extend his observational range. An alternative method

[1] Goethe made frequent use of experiments, but not in order to provide data for the immediate framing of a theory. He valued them rather as a means of displaying various aspects of a set of phenomena in relation to one another.

[2] 'We can speak of stages of initiation in philosophizing. The highest stage would be the penetration of objectivity in such a way that everything is a metaphor (cypher), nothing is without language, nothing is left to mere existence as the remains, as it were, of a non-being abandoned by God.' Karl Jaspers, *Truth and Symbol*, translated by William Kluback and Jean T. Wilde, 1959.

would be to extend the range of his own perceptual capacity: that is, to treat his own consciousness as an instrument capable of development. Hence the answer to 'How can anyone tell whether the *Urpflanze* exists?', might be, 'You will need to raise your consciousness to the level where it has its being.'[1]

One should not think of the *Urpflanze* as having to the plants a relation of cause and effect in the modern scientific sense, but as expressing itself in manifestation and withdrawal. This process is reflected in the rhythmical expansions and contractions which characterize the growth of a plant; and finally in the contraction of the flower into seed, when manifestation is reduced to a minimum and potency raised to a maximum.

This sounds suspiciously like a peculiar form of vitalism, but in fact there is an essential distinction; and a distinction also between the Goethean outlook and the rather new school of organismic biology, which recognizes the same problems that gave rise to vitalism, but deals with them in a different way.

One obvious contrast between a machine and a living organism is that a machine can be stopped and restarted without harm, and even taken to pieces and rebuilt, provided a blueprint for it exists (on paper or in someone's head). The idea of the machine is separate from the machine. In a living organism it *seems* that some kind of controlling idea is actively present within it, and inseparable from it. It was these and similar contrasts that led to vitalism; but vitalism merely *postulates* a 'vital force' or an 'entelechy' in order to account for phenomena which seem hard to explain in physical-chemical terms. Since these agencies cannot be observed, nor their effects measured, to invoke them does

---

[1] One difference between the two methods is that by using an instrument the scientist imposes a man-made device between himself and nature. What he perceives through it is not nature itself, but something abstracted or constructed from nature by his instrument. This method has proved highly effective in extending control over nature, but what is happening should be realized. The phenomena are not speaking their own language, but the man-made language of an instrument. I have even heard a scientific instrument described as 'an embodied human prejudice', but that is perhaps going a little too far.

not help research, but rather confuses it by bringing unknown variables into the picture.

L. von Bertalanffy, the leading exponent of organismic biology, is at one with vitalism in holding that when we pass from the inorganic to the living realm we need to develop new concepts; the 'mechanistic' concepts of physics and chemistry are not enough. But he insists that the phenomena of life will in time be brought under exact laws of their own, and that 'any intervention of vitalistic agents in the observable, which forms the only subject-matter of science, must be rejected'.[1]

These laws, he suggests, will be concerned with such questions as the relation of a whole to its parts, how an organism maintains a dynamic equilibrium ('steady state') with its surroundings, and how its history, its life in time, plays into its existence at any given moment. He speaks of 'dynamic morphology', and defines a living organism as 'a hierarchical order of open systems which maintains itself in the exchange of components by virtue of its system condition'.[2]

Clearly, the organismic school is nearer to the Goethean outlook than mechanistic biology is. Indeed, von Bertalanffy speaks of Goethe as 'not only a poet but also a great naturalist' and 'the founder of morphology, the science or organic forms'; and he numbers him among the 'illustrious ancestors' on whom 'the philosophy of nature of our times can look back'. But organismic biology is no more concerned than mechanistic biology is with what the phenomena themselves can teach. It, too, uses them simply as a source of concepts and thought-models; these are probably much more appropriate to the realm of life than the concepts of pure physics and chemistry can be, and they may lead to valuable extensions of predictive knowledge and power. But they remain concepts which are evolved in a scientist's head and then applied to nature; they do not lead to a more intimate *experience* of what nature is.

Von Bertalanffy is himself fully aware of this limitation:

'The physicist does not answer the question of what an electron

[1] *Problems of Life*, 1952, p. 203.   [2] Op. cit., p. 129.

really "is". His most penetrating insight only states the laws that are characteristic of the entity called an "electron". Likewise, no answer can be expected from the biologist to the question of what life may be in its "intimate essence". Even with advancing knowledge, he too will only be better able to state what laws characterize, and apply to, the phenomenon facing us as the living organism. . . . On an essentially different level lies a metaphysics trying to gain an intuitive knowledge of reality. We are not only scientific intellects, we are also human beings. To express in momentous symbols the core of reality, that is what myth, poetry and philosophy are trying.'[1]

It was just this absolute, everlasting gulf between the scientific and the artistic approaches to nature that Goethe refused to recognize. He insisted that his own method of studying nature, which was not unlike that of the artist up to a certain point, could yield valid knowledge about nature's workings. 'Up to a certain point', because after the initial stage of entering fully into experience of the phenomena, the paths of the artist and of the Goethean scientist diverge. The artist, so to speak, turns back and clothes his apprehensions in symbolic forms. His aim is not to gain conscious knowledge capable of conceptual formulation, but to create a work which will be able, by resonating at both conscious and unconscious levels in the mind of anyone who responds to it, to communicate directly something of the artist's own experience. The aim of the Goethean scientist is to penetrate 'behind the phenomena' in full consciousness and to gain understanding of how they arise from their creative sources.

Perhaps I ought to emphasize again that I am not disputing the value of the ordinary scientific method of studying nature, or setting forth the Goethean method as a superior method that ought to supersede the ordinary method in our epoch. The ordinary method—perhaps leading in biology towards organismic concepts—has an enormous amount of useful work still to do; and it is bound to absorb the attention of the vast majority of scientists for a long time to come. I am trying simply to distinguish clearly between the purposes of the two methods, the

[1] Op cit., p. 204.

first method being aimed at gaining increased control over nature, the second at gaining deeper experience of nature.

However, having made these distinctions, I do not want to imply that the two forms of science must always remain entirely separate, nor that the Goethean method can never lead to practically useful results; I believe it can and will. But these belong to a probably still fairly distant future—in fact, to that third culture in which both forms of science will exist, but in closer relationship, and perhaps with their present dominant-recessive relationship, so to speak, reversed.

It would be misleading to leave the Goethean method there, for although Goethe himself did not carry it very far, it has some far-reaching implications. When Goethe wrote of colours as 'the deeds and endurances of light', he may have meant his words to be merely metaphorical, which is of course what they are generally assumed to be. But they are more than that; they point towards a region which lies far from modern thinking but must be reached if the Goethean approach to nature is carried far enough; as it was, nearly a century after Goethe, by Rudolf Steiner.

I spoke of Goethe's types and archetypes as creative agencies or sources, but it would be better to speak of them as creative thoughts; the thoughts of creative Beings. For if the world is explored through enhanced levels of consciousness, it is found that the common notion of consciousness as somehow secondary to material forms of existence is the reverse of the truth. The consciousness of Beings is primary; nor does this apply only to the realms of life. Material substances are the crystallizations, as it were, of the creative thoughts of Beings in the past. In this way one approaches the 'meaning' of the phenomenal world by apprehending in it the purposeful thinking of the Hierarchies who manifest the will of God.

Ideas of this kind will be distasteful, if no more, to most modern scientists. Apparently one is being asked not only to go back to Goethe and take his scientific dabblings seriously, but to countenance a lot of medieval superstitions as well. This response is understandable: I have referred before to the strong conviction among scientists that to have got away from a morass of magic and fantasy is one of the great achievements of modern science— as indeed it is. I am not suggesting any reversion to medieval ways of thinking, but trying to indicate some possibilities of advance beyond the limited onlooker-range. I want now to speak of a quite modern way of thinking which does carry the Goethean outlook forward in a certain field. But anyone with a strong aversion to geometry should skip the next chapter, or most of it.

CHAPTER XVII

The Geometry of Life

There is a form of geometry, projective geometry, which has a peculiar affinity to the imaginative, mobile thinking that a Goethean approach to nature requires. Euclidean geometry deals with rigid forms; projective geometry with forms that are in continual metamorphosis, and with how forms change when they are looked at from various points of view.[1] Moreover, although projective geometry is a far from easy subject, its elements can be studied without previous mathematical training, and some people find it a helpful exercise in learning to think along these unfamiliar lines. It has a particular bearing also on the alternating expansion and contraction which characterize the growth of plants.

Projective geometry arose from the study of perspective and was gradually developed until in the nineteenth century Cayley and Klein showed it to be a very general kind of geometry, with Euclidean geometry and the various non-Euclidean geometries as special cases. At the heart of projective geometry, accordingly, we encounter the polarity (or Principle of Duality) between point and plane which is one expression of the wider polarity between contraction and expansion. The point represents maximum contraction; the plane, maximum expansion. (As an ideal entity, the plane is of infinite extent: it has no boundaries.)[2]

---

[1] More strictly, projective geometry embraces those geometrical truths which remain unchanged when we pass from one perspective to another.

[2] The Principle of Duality signifies that as point is to plane, so is plane to point, with the straight line mediating in balance between them.

Now picture a circle (or the surface of a sphere). It can be formed in two ways—radially from its point-centre, as when a circle is drawn with a compass, or peripherally by planes which, acting as tangents to its circumference, mould it from the outside:

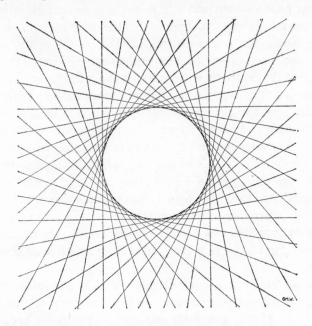

In the first case, the activity which creates the circle radiates outward from a central point: the circumference may be imagined as being held in tension by an attractive force acting from the centre. This concept can be given visible form by whirling a small weight round in a circle at the end of a piece of string held in the hand. Here the hand is the central point, and the pull of the string represents the centripetal force which holds in tension the centrifugal force of the whirling weight.

In the second case, the activity which creates the circle flows inwards from all directions at once. We must imagine the tangent planes as detaching themselves from the ideal plane at infinity and moving inwards to mould the circle. In this circle, the central point plays quite another part: it is *more like* a hollowness; but any such image must be inadequate.

I   129

It is not possible to illustrate this second process in a concrete way, as one could do in the first case with the weight circling at the end of a string. Perhaps the nearest approach to an illustration is to mould an invisible circle in the air, using one's hands as the tangent planes. Start with a large circle and gradually draw inward the moulding movement, so that the circle becomes smaller. While doing this one must imagine that at the centre of the circle one is conjuring up an expansive, out-growing potency, as though at the centre there were a seed about to sprout.[1]

This is a very rough illustration of the second way of forming a circle, from the outside in, and there is a decisive reason why this second way cannot be represented in physically visible terms. For the first way, in which the centre point is the active, originating agency, corresponds to the way in which physical forces—gravity and the potential force implied in 'momentum' are the most obvious examples—operate in the Euclidean space of our everyday experience. The weight flying round at the end of the string is a picture of how a satellite is kept orbiting the earth under the pull of gravity, which is regarded as operating from centre to centre.

The second way of circle-forming corresponds geometrically to a quite other kind of space, the polar opposite of Euclidean space; and of this anti-Euclidean space, or negative space, we have no direct experience. Hence the planar way of circle-forming can only be adumbrated by a makeshift procedure which should be regarded not as an illustration, but as an aid to an exercise of thought. We can *think* negative-Euclidean space; otherwise a consistent geometry of it would never have been developed. However, the existence of such a geometry does not prove that negative-Euclidean spaces exist in our universe, but only that they *could* exist, in which case we must imagine

---

[1] Geometrically speaking, when the planes are acting as tangents to mould the circumference of the circle, the polar points, severally corresponding to them with respect to the given circle, are on the circumference. If the planes are then imagined to recede again, expanding outwards in all directions towards the periphery, the polar points move inwards. When the planes are again merged into the plane at infinity, the points have become the centre of the circle.

THE GEOMETRY OF LIFE

them as imperceptibly interpenetrating Euclidean space everywhere.

As is well known, several other mathematically consistent non-Euclidean geometries have been worked out, and which geometry applies to our everyday space has to be determined by observation and measuring, not by pure mathematics.[1] Negative-Euclidean geometry, however, is a special case, for the type of space it represents is not an alternative to Euclidean space, but a possible counterpart of it, a kind of 'negative twin'. Both forms of space *could* exist in the same universe. But whether negative-Euclidean spaces do actually exist in our universe is a question for observation and experiment.

Again, the existence of Euclidean space does not *prove* that a force of gravity must operate in it; gravity is inferred from observations as a way of explaining phenomena. Similarly, if negative-Euclidean spaces do exist, this would not *prove* that they give rise to an expansive force—a force originating at the periphery and active particularly in all seed-points of growth. Hence these conceptions are hypotheses only; they have been advanced as a basis for interpreting in a new way certain biological phenomena, connected especially with growth and organ-formation, in plants, animals and man.[2] The question is whether they fit the observed facts better than any other hypothesis.

[1] To call the expansive force 'anti-gravity' would be misleading, for this would imply that it functions as the opposite of gravity in Euclidean space—the 'anti-grav.' familiar in science-fiction. Its functioning is of a quite different character and can occur only in—or rather as part of—negative Euclidean space.

[2] For a short introduction to this aspect of projective geometry, see George Adams, 'Space and Counter-Space', contributed to the Rudolf Steiner centenary symposium, *The Faithful Thinker* (London, 1961). See also George Adams (G. A. Kaufmann), *Strahlende Weltgestaltung*, Dornach 1933; *Physical and Ethereal Spaces*, 'Anthroposophy' Quarterly, vol. VIII, 1933; and, with Olive Whicher, *The Living Plant and the Science of Physical and Ethereal Spaces*, 1949); *The Plant between Sun and Earth*, 1952 (Goethean Science Foundation, Clent, Worcestershire); and *Die Pflanze in Raum und Gegenraum*, Stuttgart, 1960. Also L. Locher-Ernst, *Projektive Geometrie und die Grundlagen der Euklidischen und Polareuklidischen Geometrie*, Orell-Füssli Verlag, Zurich, 1940; and *Raum und Gegenraum*, Dornach, 1957. These authors acknowledge their indebtedness to Rudolf Steiner; see *inter alia* two lectures given by Dr. Steiner at

The ground is fairly open; in this realm of growth and form (including embryonic growth) many problems remain. Some of the processes involved can be followed step by step and perhaps explained in biochemical terms, but exactly how the parts of a living organism come to take the forms and positions they do, and how they are related to each other and to the whole, is in most instances not yet clearly understood. During growth they often seem to behave as if they were controlled by some kind of morphogenetic field, though no firm evidence for the existence of any such chemico-physical field as would account for the phenomena has yet been found. The geometry of negative-Euclidean space *might* turn out to be the geometry that belongs to the realm of life, just as Euclidean geometry belongs to the realm of the lifeless.[1]

In writing about projective geometry I have obviously attempted no more than a brief glance at the first elements of an intricate subject. There are two reasons for doing this. First, because of the bearing of projective geometry on the Goethean approach to

The Hague, 8/9 April 1922, published in the volume *Die Bedeutung der Anthroposophie*, Dornach, 1957, and in translation in *The Golden Blade* annual, 1961; also the opening chapters of *Fundamentals of Therapy*, by Rudolf Steiner and Ita Wegman, 1925.

[1] Early in the nineteenth century, when Poncelet and others were developing the new projective form of geometry, the great French mathematician, Michel Chasles, undertook a review of the whole history of geometry from ancient times. In his *Aperçu Historique sur l'Origine et le Développement des Méthodes en Géometrie* (Brussels, 1837), which soon became a classic, he wrote (I translate from the third edition, 1889): 'We shall be led, I believe, to recognise . . . that a universal duality is the great law of nature, reigning wherever human knowledge extends. . . . Can one even foresee where the consequences of such a principle of duality would end? After having linked in pairs all the phenomena of nature, and the mathematical laws which govern them, may not this principle lead on to the very causes of these phenomena? And could one not then say that to the law of gravitation there might well correspond another law, playing an equal part with Newton's law and, like the latter, serving to explain celestial phenomena? Or if, on the contrary, the law of gravitation proved to be its own 'dual' counterpart—as are some propositions in the duality of space as such—this would be yet another cogent proof that it is indeed the supreme and unique law of the universe.'

nature, and the indication it gives that this approach is not vaguely sentimental, but has aspects which lend themselves to mathematical treatment. Secondly, because both the Goethean approach and projective geometry itself have an artistic quality, and I believe this quality will and should become more active in the science of the future.

But to bring science and art into closer relation will not be easy, for art has a very uncertain status in the onlooker-age.

CHAPTER XVIII

Quiet in the Head

In early epochs, many people probably gained from the outer world something akin to the experience that we gain from works of art. It was more dreamlike and less critical: the world spoke to them in symbols and pictures formed in their minds. The function of art, then, was not so much to heighten individual experience as to combine with religion in rituals and monuments design to maintain the community in fruitful relationship with the realm of the gods. Thus the artist had a well-recognized social status and function. In Western Europe he began to lose these when art drew apart from religion and became mainly a secular entertainment or decoration, dependent on the patronage of princes. But his situation became problematical only with the rise of the new analytical science and the advance of technology, leading on to the Industrial Revolution. In the commercialized society of the nineteenth century, artists had to justify their activities: it was not obvious that they were either adding to the nation's wealth or contributing to the stock of useful knowledge—what were they really after?

Many artists were of course content to produce works that brought them a living; and there were some (Dickens, for example) who criticized social abuses and yet were popular and rewarded. I am concerned here with those who would not or could not come to terms with society and so formed the dissenting aesthetic movements of their time.

The Romantic movement was the first of these; later came its more consciously theorizing successor, the Symbolist movement;

later again the aestheticism of the nineties, the Imagists, Vorticism, Cubism, Surrealism. . . . They were in many ways diverse but had one aim in common: to show that a work of art has a 'meaning' different from and superior to its superficial meaning as a representation or description of something in the outer world. They held that to apprehend this inner 'meaning' was an experience valuable in itself, and that a work of art had therefore a function and a value independent of its utility or its commercial success.

> *Full fathom five thy father lies,*
> *Of his bones are coral made.* . . .

How do these lines differ in meaning from a factual prose statement about a drowned parent? Perhaps the basic distinction is that they operate differently on the mind. They bring about a temporary change in consciousness, so that something embodied in the lines—not only in their verbal meaning but in their sound and rhythm and associated overtones and images—is perceived; something essential that can only be perceived directly and not described in other terms. The experience may be accompanied by emotion, but it is fundamentally an essence, not a feeling, that is communicated to the mind by a work of art.[1] The essence is not separate from the ordinary meaning, but emerges from it and returns to illuminate it.

This implies that the normal average level of consciousness is inadequate for apprehending the inner significance of a work of art. Perhaps this has always been true to some extent, but it applies especially to the onlooker-consciousness. The aesthetic movements of the last hundred years have been a reaction both against the commercial values of industrial society and against the mode of consciousness which accompanies them (and helps to create them). Thus we have become familiar with the artist as a 'bohemian' figure, a rebel against conventional society: he is contemptuous of it and claims to live—or at least to work—by superior and more or less esoteric standards of his own.

A tendency nowadays is to condemn these attitudes, to regard

[1] Cf. Suzanne K. Langer, *Feeling and Form*, 1953.

them as rather silly, to say that a serious artist must be *engagé*, and so on. But I think the situation they reflect will not be easily remedied by exhortation or education or by the Arts Council.[1] For the isolation of the modern artist from the general public is a symptom of the divided mode of consciousness which belongs to the onlooker-age. It is a mode in which the conscious part of the mind is more wide-awake and selfconscious than it was in earlier epochs, and also cut off from the unconscious by a stronger, more resistant threshold.

Where is this threshold to be found? Generally it is thought of in purely psychological terms; it has no clearly recognized location in the bodily organism. We are all, however, aware of degrees of consciousness, and these are associated with bodily regions. We are most brightly conscious, most wide-awake, in the head. We are dimly conscious—half-awake and dreaming as it were— in the region of the chest; thus we have a slight, intermittent awareness of our heart-beats and our breathing, and it is here that bodily symptoms of emotion are most readily evident. Under emotional stress our heart-beat quickens and our breathing changes, or we may 'catch our breath'.

Of course we should not become aware of these symptoms if they were not signalled through the nerves to the brain, but neither the symptoms nor the feelings seem to belong to the head. The impression we have is of feelings surging up from the chest region, or of an oppression there of feelings we are unable to express or dare not admit:

> *Canst thou not . . .*
> *Cleanse the stuff'd bosom of that perilous stuff*
> *Which weighs upon the heart?*

Thus a kind of partial threshold, often crossed in both directions, seems to lie between the head and the chest. Below the chest lies a threshold which is not normally crossed at all: in health we

---

[1] It can be forcibly remedied by enlisting the artists as servants of the State, but this merely suppresses the problem by conventionalizing the art.

are not conscious of the continuous metabolic activities concerned with the digestion and utilization of food. They provide the energy for muscular exertion and other acts of will; they may be a bodily picture of psychic activities in the unconscious depths of the mind.[1]

Nowadays a prevailing view is that there are no specific acts of 'will', and no sense in speaking of 'conation' on an equal footing with cognition. Perhaps this is because the workings of the will are often obscure, not easy to distinguish from impulse and desire. But how should we describe the direction of attention towards one object or another?

I am sitting in my room and I focus my attention first on a table, then on the window, then on a bookcase. A more difficult but similar exercise is to pick out one strand in a piece of concerted music. Or I can focus inwardly on a particular image or train of thought. In all such cases the impression I have is that I am turning a beam of attention, as it were, on to something, and that I am free to turn it in whatever direction I choose. I am not saying that this simple experience is evidence of 'free will' in a metaphysical sense, but I don't know how to describe what I do except as an act of will. It would seem far-fetched to interpret all such acts as inevitable responses to urges, conscious or unconscious, for I can direct my attention in turn to a series of objects, all equally uninteresting and commonplace.

In these cases, where we are willing only to notice something, the bodily foundations of the will are not directly evident. But they can become evident—on occasions of crisis, for instance, when something seems to rise up from far down inside us, not from the head nor from the heart, and gives us the will to act. Or, if we are afraid and feel that the demand is more than we can meet, we experience a sinking feeling, a feeling of 'goneness', in the same lower region.[2]

---

[1] These connections of thinking, feeling and willing with bodily functions were first adumbrated in a book by Rudolf Steiner, *Von Seelenrätseln* (1917), and later developed by him in various ways.

[2] A different way of getting an impression of the nature of will is to press firmly with one hand—preferably keeping the eyes shut—against a piece of matter that will not budge. The pure experience then is not of a

Experiences of this kind have left their mark on popular language: thus we say that a man 'has guts' or 'lacks guts', or that he 'has no stomach for a fight', and it would still be intelligible to call him 'lily-livered'. These phrases probably derive from a time when consciousness was felt to be less concentrated in the head than it is with us. We can make no sense of 'willing' because of the increased separation of conscious island from unconscious sea.

This threefold picture of the human organism has a bearing on the history of the onlooker-consciousness and the kind of thinking associated with it. The picture shows an evident contrast, a polarity, between the head and the metabolic region. The head of course has its own metabolism, but this is unobtrusive; we *experience* the head as a kind of cool open space in which there is room to think. If we could become conscious of the breaking down and building up processes in the digestive system, we should be confused and overwhelmed, perhaps very painfully, by the energetic activities—the energy-exchanges—ceaselessly going on. It would be rather like leaving a sheltered office for the racket of a factory with furnaces in full blast.

Intermediate between the poles, and so intermediate also in its relation to thinking, is the chest region. If we become abnormally conscious of our heart-beats, through palpitation perhaps, or if exertion leaves us panting for breath, we can still think, but to think clearly and coherently becomes difficult. These physical effects are paralleled by the influence of feeling on thinking: we have to keep our feelings in check if we are to think accurately, without bias.

These schematic divisions are of course not absolute: thinking is never quite free from feeling and willing, nor feeling from thinking, and so on. But it remains on the whole true that thinking requires the shelter of the head in order to function properly,

material object—that is something known conceptually in advance—but of resistance, counter-pressure. Here the human will encounters that form of materially embodied will, not its own, which perhaps makes for what we call inertia.

in accordance with its own nature. Moreover, the head is physio-
logically well adapted to provide this quiet atmosphere. It is
composed—apart from the face and outer sense-organs—largely
of bone and nerve-tissue, the most inert elements in the body, the
parts with the least capacity for regeneration after injury. It is as
though the tumultuous forces of life draw back in order to make
room for clear consciousness.[1]

We feel that we do our thinking in this bony retreat, this place
of the skull. We have, so to speak, arrived there after a long evolutionary journey during which thinking has only gradually acquired its modern character—a character essential for the use of
the scientific method, which requires no ardent faith and must
take care to guard itself against emotional bias.

Modern man is of course still subject to all sorts of irrational
impulses, evident in his conduct and his emotional life, and in
his thinking too. But in the quiet retreat of his head he *can*
think freely, in a way he could not while he retained something of a participating consciousness, and his sense-perceptions
spoke to his thinking with a meaning of their own. Because he
is now able to stand detached from the world and to perceive
it simply as a collection of passive objects, he can think freely
about it and form whatever conceptual models of it he may
need. The outcome of his free thinking is the astonishing new
world of technology—there has been nothing like it on the earth
before.

But in order to live, people need more than this: they need to
find some purpose in life and some meaning in the world. The
pure onlooker-consciousness cannot of itself meet these needs:
the world disclosed to it is incredibly vast and marvellously

[1] 'The ancient peoples, though in no way more stupid than ourselves,
had not yet begun to use the cerebral part of the mind, the last gift of
evolution, in cold detachment from the emotions and the imaginative
creations gushing up into consciousness from more primitive sources.
The rational intellect, man's highest and most dangerous faculty, had to
be set free and cultivated before true philosophy, science, and its violent
and uncontrollable child, industry, could be brought into the world.'
Jacquetta Hawkes, *Man on Earth*, 1954.

intricate, but neither in galaxies nor in atoms is there any human significance to be discerned.

Nor is there meaning to be found by looking within; the content of the onlooker-consciousness is a kind of emptiness, a natural home for doubt and scepticism. Descartes, trying to get down to something indubitable—'bastir dans un fons qui est tout à moy' —may have believed he had done so with his 'cogito, ergo sum', but critics have remarked that the Latin conceals an illegitimate use of 'I'; he had no sure ground for saying more than 'thinking exists'. Indeed, there is a sense in which he might have more justly said, 'I think, therefore I *am* not', echoing Hamlet's 'sicklied o'er with the pale cast of thought'.

It is this characteristic of the onlooker-consciousness which has led to the various reactions against it: notably that of D. H. Lawrence, who struggled during most of his life to explain what he meant by living in the blood and loins, not always shut up in the head. To many young intellectuals of the period his doctrine (and not only his writing) made a potent appeal; they responded to it largely because they felt that their own ways of living and thinking were impoverished and unfertile—

> Le vent se lève! . . . il faut tenter de vivre!
> L'air immense ouvre et referme mon livre. . . .

Lawrence was greatly preoccupied with sex, but his best writing, I would say, is concerned with the world of nature, with scenes and landscapes, birds and beasts. In him the older form of participating consciousness was still present as a natural gift:

'He looked at things with the eyes, so it seemed, of a man who has been at the brink of death and to whom, as he emerges from the darkness, the world reveals itself as unfathomably beautiful and mysterious. For Lawrence, existence was one continuous convalescence; it was as though he were newly reborn from a mortal illness every day of his life. . . . A walk with him in the country was a walk through the marvellously rich and significant landscape which is at once the background and the principal personage of all his novels. He seemed to know, by personal experience, what it was like to be a tree or a daisy or a breaking wave or even the mysterious moon itself.'[1]

But Lawrence was also a clever man—very good at examinations in his youth—and I think there was a chronic friction between these two aspects of his nature. He would probably not have hated modern intellectuals so much if he had not been partly one himself. His violent outbursts of fury and the occasional malice which bedevilled his personal relationships were perhaps an expression of his inability to resolve his own inner conflict. He wanted to live in community with a few chosen friends, but round him there was always a whirlpool of jealousies and resentments. He sought all over the world for peasants or primitive people still imbued with the old consciousness, but after living close to any of them for a while he generally recoiled from their 'mindlessness'. Finally he gave his praise to the ancient Etruscans, judging their ways of life from fragmentary well-paintings and statues; they could not disillusion him, being all long dead.

Lawrence believed (though he used a different terminology, often turgid and misleading) that a participating form of consciousness is necessary for the good life; and his genius has left us some wonderful impressions of what this way of experiencing the world can mean. But the wish to revive an older form of consciousness is always in vain.

[1] Aldous Huxley, from the introduction to his edition of *The Letters of D. H. Lawrence*, 1932.

CHAPTER XIX

Freedom and Fraternity

It is not only artists and writers who rebel against the effects of the onlooker-consciousness. Its unsocial character, its tendency to enclose the individual in himself, a prey to scepticism and unsure purpose, have led also to social reactions against it.

The totalitarian movements of our time are an example. They are confusing; Fascism and Communism have some elements in common and are yet very different in outlook and aims. Fascism dreams nostalgically of the past; it is suspicious of the modern intellect and not at ease with modern science. In some respects it tries to do on a national scale what Lawrence tried to do in individual terms. Communism worships science—or at least technology—and has its eyes set with unbounded optimism on the future.

Both movements are authoritarian: they assign to the individual his articles of faith and define his obligations towards the national goal. And both set out to infuse meaning and purpose into life by drawing everyone into communal activities. In so doing they supply in a distorted, compulsive form an element often missing from the atomized society characteristic of the onlooker-consciousness—the element of co-operation, or fraternity.

During the nineteenth century, in the early heyday of industrial capitalism, this element was driven underground, repressed, by the efforts of the ruling class to ban the beginnings of trade unionism. The early unions had to fight for life; their fraternity became that of an army, the militant working-class.

Marx turned the fact of class-conflict into a doctrine, and the Communism he founded on it had the driving-force of a repressed impulse struggling to break free. But the course it took was not what the early trade unionists, at least in this country, had expected or desired. In their aspirations, fraternity and liberty were not opposed, but (perhaps often rather confusedly) conjoined.

I believe that a society in which they are conjoined in harmony is the form of society which ought to develop from later stages of the onlooker-consciousness epoch, but to bring it about is a task which the onlooker-consciousness cannot at present achieve. It amounts to something like a reconciling of conscious with unconscious, for freedom is the essential requirement of modern thinking, while the impulse for fraternity springs from the unconscious, from the region of the will. Fraternity is fostered not by thinking together—intellectuals are notoriously fissiparous—but by working together.[1]

Fraternity belongs in one form to the past, to epochs prior to the individualism of the onlooker-stage, and in another, potential form to the future. Perhaps it will one day mean more than co-operation, more than a general feeling of brotherhood; it may mean that a man will find it impossible to sit down to a full meal if his neighbour is in want. Somewhere in Communism there has been an aspiration towards this future fraternity; but present-day Communism does not try to reconcile fraternity with freedom, as the West understands freedom, and I doubt if they can be reconciled unless the third element in the famous slogan, equality, is brought in as a mediator between the poles.[2]

Equality is a confusing idea; what can it realistically mean?

There are so many ways in which human beings are unequal, and no very obvious way in which they are equal. Scientifically—i.e. genetically—it is plainly not true (in spite of the famous statement in the American Constitution) that men are born equal; and a thoroughly scientific method of social planning would be bound

[1] Feeling does not *necessarily* make for fraternity. In itself it has a fluctuating character, flowing and ebbing between sympathy and antipathy; akin to the ebb and flow of breathing and the systole and diastole of the heart.

[2] Cf. *The Three Spheres of Society*, by Charles Waterman, 1946.

to recognize the facts of inequality and to build upon them. The aim would be to give everyone the best education (but no more) that he or she could profit by, and then to assign each person by aptitude tests to the kind of job suited to his or her ability and temperament. The result would be a hierarchical society, with full equality of opportunity, and thereafter a strict grading of authority, status and reward.[1]

Yet the idea of equality is deeply rooted in the social aspirations of the West: it must mean *something*. Indeed it is given partial effect in certain fields: in adult suffrage and in the aim (never perfectly achieved) of equality before the law. There is no logic in a system of voting which allows each individual voter, however brilliant or brainless, to carry equal weight; but it answers to a feeling for what is right and fair.

This feeling, if expressed in social institutions, is able to mediate between liberty and fraternity by preventing either from running to extremes. Give liberty its head and you get exploitations of the weak by the powerful, including of course exploitation of workers by employers. Give fraternity its head and you get a tendency for the exceptional individual to be hated and feared; the emphasis is on conformity and mediocrity; on the submergence of the individual in the mass. A feeling for equality insists on the right of the individual to be himself, to be whatever he can, as long as he does not exploit others; it protects him against both extremes.

Before a feeling for equality can be given social expression, however, it must effectively exist; and I think it is ultimately a religious feeling. A scientific humanist could argue that certain equal rights are recognized in society because it is convenient for everyone (or for most people) that they should be: everyone wants the law to be impartial in case he comes up against it himself, and adult suffrage is a useful safeguard against discontent. But I do not think the aspiration for equality could be sustained solely on them; in a rationally planned society the inducements to promote efficiency at the expense of equality would be too strong.

[1] Cf. *The Rise of the Meritocracy*, by Michael Young, 1958.

The religious feeling I mean is not exclusively Christian, but it has been given form and force by Christianity in such words as 'children of one Father'. Unless persons are recognized to be not only what they appear to be in the flesh, these words have no meaning. Their implication is that in every human being there is a spark of the Divine, and that this is something to which conceptions of inequality have no relevance. If a strong and clever man is really to regard a weak and foolish man as his equal, he must hold and act on the belief that what they have in common—*ex Deo nascimur*—is more important and enduring than what sets them apart.

This belief can obviously not be held by Communists, and hardly by scientific humanists. Nor is it one that the onlooker-consciousness can easily arrive at by itself. But unless such a belief gains fresh strength from a renewal of its old sources, then I think the future trend of society will be away from liberal-individualistic forms, in which the idea of equality survives as a heritage from a declining religious past, towards collective forms in which the individual will count for less and less. This is already beginning to happen in all highly industrialized countries, whatever their politics, if only because the scale of modern production and the efficient use of science call for large organizations and a great deal of collective enterprise.

If this trend continues, and is not resisted by an effective counter-current, the collective forms of the future will either be Communist or will share with Communism the need to promote a spurious kind of fraternity (perhaps called the 'company spirit') at some cost to liberty.[1] Since many persons will be figuring as units in industrial projects or economic plans, the tendency will be to treat them as units ('manpower', 'man-hours', 'personnel'), and there will be no imperative reason for not doing so.

An imperative reason could spring from a feeling for the transcendental equality of human beings, but that would call for a picture of man very different from the scientific one, which reflects the limitations of the modern consciousness. Unless these

---

[1] Cf. *The Organization Man*, by W. H. Whyte, 1957; also *The Lonely Crowd*, by David Riesman, 1950.

limits are surpassed, we may find that we are moving towards a society in which the creations of technology will increasingly determine the character of human living; a society in which human beings would be largely occupied in serving the demands of machines.[1] If there were still some errant desires or rebellious ambitions, these could be handled with improved tranquillizer drugs, designed to promote not merely contentment but a permanent mild euphoria. Life would pass by like a not unpleasant dream.

This forward view may be too sombre; I have no doubt that science will continue to learn from its own mistakes. Nor do I underestimate the extraordinary resilience of the human spirit. But although the human spirit cannot readily be crushed, it can be darkened, imprisoned; and an age of great technological brilliance can be an age of spiritual darkness. The onlooker-consciousness, finely adapted to scientific exploration in certain fields, does tend to imprison the human spirit and to shut it off from light. We can learn more about this from the growing-up of a child.

[1] In science-fiction one can read of future cities built under vast domes which shut out the weather and ensure a constant air-conditioned climate. In I. Asimov's *The Naked Sun* (1958), people have come to dread any exposure to the unnatural 'outside', and a character who has to travel (in a sealed spaceship) to a distant planet can hardly bear, on arrival, his first sight of the open sky. E. M. Forster's early story, *The Machine Stops*, had a rather similar theme.

CHAPTER XX

Seven Years

Few people now regard childhood as a time of bliss and innocence. It is a time of intensities: intense struggles and anxieties, intense experiences of fear and joy, frustration, guilt and pride. It could hardly be otherwise, when so much growing and learning and adaptation has to be got through in a few years.

If in adult life we could vividly relive this whole experience of growing up, from infancy onwards, the idea of the evolution of consciousness would probably seem less strange. We should not learn just what the consciousness of early men was like, if only because early men were adult and sexually mature. But growing up does recapitulate in its own way some phases in the long evolution which has led to the onlooker mode.

There are three broad stages—infancy, childhood, adolescence —each lasting about seven years. They should be regarded, I believe, as a process whereby the individuality of the child gradually enters into and takes possession of the bodily organism.[1] There can be no proof that this picture is true, but anyone who observes a growing child will find nothing incompatible with it and a good deal that may seem to confirm it. All I shall attempt here is a brief sketch of how growing up looks from this point of view. Many details and variations and qualifications will be left out; they can be found elsewhere.[2]

[1] This implies a line of spiritual heredity distinct from physical heredity; some childhood illnesses may reflect a struggle to reconcile the two.

[2] See A. C. Harwood, *The Way of a Child* (third edition, 1952); *The*

147

Can we really know anything about an infant's state of consciousness during the very early years? This may well seem doubtful, but the immensely patient studies carried out by child psychologists[1] in various countries do give grounds for plausible inferences, allowing for the fact that infantile experiences cannot be precisely rendered in adult terms.

A very young infant lives most actively in and through his limbs and his metabolism; he kicks and stretches and sucks. An object is not real to him unless he can handle it and preferably put it in his mouth; seeing is not enough. To begin with, he does not distinguish clearly the outer world from his own world of immediate sensations. The outer world brings him impressions of light and colour and noise, of constriction and freedom, deprivation or satisfaction; but at first all such impressions are as though part of a continuous dream. He learns not by taking conscious thought, but chiefly by imitation and practice—which is how any activity involving the limbs and muscles has to be learnt.

He has powerful feelings, but they are bound up with his bodily needs and appetites. A young infant parted from his mother may not seem to miss her, but often he will react by ceasing to thrive or by actually falling ill. Later on, when he begins to walk and talk, his feelings will express themselves more directly, but his anger, jealousy or delight are like winds that sweep through him; he can be quickly distracted from one feeling to another. The affection he seems to show is more the sign of an organic need than a consciously recognized sentiment. Hence the folly of trying to prod a young child into avowals of personal affection ('Do you love mummy, darling?'). Of course, this kind of prodding is always silly and sometimes cruel; but it does not even make sense before a true capacity for personal affection has been born.

Nor should a young child be prodded into precocious shows of

Recovery of Man in Childhood, 1958. In his Preface to *The Way of a Child* Mr. Harwood says: 'This little book is entirely based on the study of Rudolf Steiner's books and lectures on childhood and education and on many years' experience as a teacher in a school founded to carry out his ideas.'

[1] e.g., Bühler, Gesell, Klein, Piaget, Shirley, Valentine, Susan Isaacs.

cleverness. His immediate experience of the world is too vivid and compelling for him to be able to stand over against it and analyse it intellectually.

This does not mean that a young child never *can* think logically. He certainly can and does, about simple practical matters within his competence. Nowadays, too, many children are encouraged, or stimulated by a mainly grown-up environment, to develop ways of talking which make them seem, on occasion, painfully like little adults. But learning through the brain is not a young child's natural bent: it is better for him not to be driven to learn reading or writing until after the change of teeth.

During these early years a child has in any event to go through strenuous and generally unspoken emotional conflicts connected with parental images and fantasies; these are later forgotten, but they live on in his unconscious, and how he has coped with them —how far they remain unresolved, not related to reality—may have great influence on his future development, right into adult life. His prime need in these years—a need now widely recognized —is for a background of security and undemanding affection, with plenty of natural opportunities to learn through imitation and play. What he learns in this way—e.g. from watching how his parents behave, not only towards him but towards each other— will influence him much more deeply than precepts or admonitions.

After the change of teeth a new stage begins. The next seven years can be the most harmonious phase of growing up, until puberty casts its shadow. (The 'latency period', intervening between infantile sexuality and adolescence, is part of this.) But a great deal depends on whether these years are recognized and treated as a stage valuable in itself, and not turned into an anxious time of cramming for exams.

New capacities for feeling and thinking are released; it is the time for fairy-tales and legends, and later for myths of heroes and gods; the matter-of-fact stories which suit younger children are no longer enough. The active imagination which produced the myths reappears in the child; they speak to him somewhat as they spoke to the peoples among whom they were born. It is the time, too, for hero-worship; the time when a child needs an authority he can respect and trust—the same authority that in adolescence he will repudiate. It is from the consciousness of these years that we can best understand what it meant to live in the heroic age, when loyalty to one's chieftain was the first duty and a magical aura surrounded the persons of kings.[1]

During this period thinking becomes more coherent and consecutive, but it runs to pictures and images rather than to logical concepts; thinking and feeling are still interfused. Hence it is not surprising that so many children show remarkable artistic gifts at this stage; and teachers often sadly observe how transient these gifts are—after a few years the imagination fades out of the paintings and the verses. Gifts of this kind will of course continue to develop strongly only in children with a definite artistic bent, but it is not inevitable that in other children they should entirely disappear. Generally they do so because the education during these years is prematurely intellectual—partly in content but still more in style and form.

In conventional prep. schools (they still exist) activities are divided mainly between intellectual subjects, taught with an eye fixed firmly on the 'common entrance', and outdoor games taken with ludicrous seriousness. This means that one of the three organic systems—the rhythmic system, connected with feeling and artistic impulses—is ignored.[2] Only the head and limbs are taught and exercised, and quite separately, with nothing to mediate between them, as the rhythmic system can do. These methods, carried on through the public schools, have helped to create a wider gulf between highbrows and hearties in this country than in most others.

In State schools, with too few opportunities for games, there has been less emphasis on them, but the State system is no less

[1] These years are also the time of tribal association, when boys go in for little gangs and semi-secret societies. For adolescent youths to live in gangs may often be a sign of retardation. Adolescence should be the time for clubs—sports clubs and the like—non-compulsory associations with a different character and purpose.
[2] See Chapter XVIII.

effective in distorting the second seven-year period. Children are not normally ready for much purely abstract thinking until after puberty, but under the combined pressure of the eleven-plus and an early leaving-age they are not free to wait. Their brains and memories are drilled; their powers of feeling and imagination are starved. What is really needed during this period is that all the teaching should be given as far as possible an artistic quality (or one might say a rhythmical, musical quality), with nothing presented in a dry, purely intellectual way.[1]

During the past fifty years there have been enormous advances, almost a revolution, in attitudes towards children and schooling, not only outside the State sector but within it; old conventions and traditions are far less powerful; the arts are increasingly regarded as an essential part of education and not merely as optional 'extras'. But the distorting pressures remain; they cannot be wished away, nor overcome by the devotion of teachers. They arise from an educational system which is part of a social system; they illustrate the conflict always liable to arise between social-economic demands and the human needs of children. Our society asks for efficiency and economy in education, combined—at least in theory—with equality of opportunity. What in practice do these demands mean?

If equality of opportunity means that no child should suffer educationally through lack of means or because of social barriers, it is certainly right. But when it is coupled with a demand for efficiency, it can work out cruelly: it leads to 'streaming' almost from the start, to a tripartite secondary system, to the segregation and training of a future *élite*, and so to a new kind of class system based not on ancestry or wealth but on inexorable grading in terms of IQ. But during school years the children should be learning how to live together, as in the world they will have to do: the clever and the stupid, the timid and the ambitious, side by side. From *this* point of view they ought not to be streamed and segregated; all the children in the same age-group ought to share

[1] For practical examples, see A. C. Harwood, *The Recovery of Man in Childhood*, op. cit.

some main lessons at least; and those with a low IQ will not feel hopelessly inferior if they are treated as full members of the group, and whatever other capacities they have are noticed and brought out. Ideally, a school should no more discriminate between its children than a good mother does; in her eyes, however unequal their endowments, they are all of equal worth. In the schools of a truly humane society there would be no intelligence tests, no streaming, no decisive exams; the teachers would be free to judge the individual needs of the children and to adapt the teaching accordingly.

But under present conditions, with overcrowded classes and the eleven-plus or the G.C.E. looming ahead, no such ideals can be realized, or even approached, in most schools; and while a nation has to compete for its living in a world of dangerous armed rivalries, its educational system is bound to be profoundly influenced by 'what the country needs'. The distorting pressures will remain; all we can do is to be at least conscious of them, to recognize their effects and to look for ways of mitigating them here and there.

One effect of mishandling the second seven-year period is that for many children, unless they are gifted and ambitious, later education becomes tedious; they want to escape from it as soon as they can. But when they go out into the world, it too seems tedious and meaningless; they look to manufactured excitements and distractions to fill the void, or they may express their resentment by engaging in aimless destructiveness.

These reactions would be less common if the powers of feeling and imagination in so many children had not been starved and stunted at school. For these are the powers that bring wonder into our experience of the world, and through which the world gains meaning and value for us. In young children these powers are never lacking; the world never seems dull to them. It is during the period leading up to puberty that the change occurs; the capacity for imaginative response is so often lost.

I am not suggesting that the second seven-year period should be regarded as an idyllic time, or that in the schools it should be devoted to nothing but delightful artistic pursuits. It is not all idyllic, by any means; it is for example the time when children are much given to forming little gangs through which they persecute rivals and bully outsiders. Quite young children are often cruel, but in an unthinking way; conscious cruelty and the enjoyment of it begin in this second period. In fact, this period is marked particularly by that fall from 'innocence' into 'experience' which will reach a certain climax at puberty. Hence there should be no question of keeping the children sheltered in a garden of artistic delights, but rather of helping them to prepare for their expulsion from it.

In practice, this means that education has to aim at leading children 'down to earth', while keeping alive their capacity for imaginative response. This approach will be expressed both in the extended range of subjects taught (with science included in the later part of the period) and in the treatment of them. The aim will be to start always with directly observable phenomena, not with theory, so that abstract thinking, now incipient, may not lose touch with first-hand experience and practical experiment. Puberty comes with less of a shock if intellectual growth has not been precociously stimulated in unnatural separation from aesthetic feeling and manual skill. And this separation often paves the way for the 'two cultures' to fall apart later on.

In organic terms, puberty means that the individuality takes full possession of the body; the ego experiences a strengthening and surging up of the passions and the will. In terms of consciousness, the child, now ceasing to be a child, becomes more sharply aware of himself as an independent person; he feels impelled to challenge authority, parental authority first of all, but without feeling really sure of his ground. His enhanced selfconsciousness and his unspoken new desires make him shy and awkward; his own shadow falls between him and the world.

In our epoch, puberty means something more. The youth becomes in some degree an onlooker; he enters into the virtues and limitations of this mode of consciousness. He acquires a new capacity for exact thinking; but when for him the familiar questions arise, explicitly or in some disguise—'What am I doing here—what is the meaning of life?'—he will not be satisfied with the answers given by an accepted creed. The onlooker-consciousness calls for answers that can be 'proved on the pulses', yet in itself it brings no experience which throws light on *these* questions. If the youth is scientifically-minded, he may find the world full of fascinating interest; he may be ready to spend his life in exploring it and gaining power over it; but the world he explores will be mute and impersonal; it will not answer the questions of the heart.

An adolescent who thus experiences the onlooker-consciousness has come a long way from childhood. In his early years he will not have found the world devoid of meaning; on the contrary, it spoke to him with so many voices that he had to struggle to identify himself as distinct from it. Today, the typical adolescent stands apart from the world, looking at it—a modern scientific world. He has to relate himself to it and to find meaning in it by his own efforts, if he can.

D. H. Lawrence hated science because he felt it to be hostile to the participating consciousness he had retained, and from his own point of view he was right; this mode of consciousness has to undergo a kind of death before it can be reborn in a form compatible with the hard-won virtues of the scientific approach. It is similar with the imaginative consciousness of early childhood. What should be aimed at is to offer the child an upbringing and an education such that a seed from this early imaginative life will be carried on through puberty into adolescence, and will presently find opportunity to flower again in a new adult mode.

The history of human consciousness is paralleled here. The world that once was rich in meaning has become like a flat dropscene; it needs to be recreated through human endeavour, the imaginative endeavour which Blake associated with the building of Jerusalem. But we have always to reckon with the shadow of puberty, for this too has its parallel in the history of man.

CHAPTER XXI

Rise and Fall

Puberty has always been recognized as a critical transition, but in earlier epochs the experience of it will have been different, for adult consciousness had not then reached its present mode. It is in fairly modern times that the feeling of something precious lost with the passing of childhood—the 'shades of the prison-house'—seems to have become acute. What I believe is being experienced here is a late consequence, almost a final working-out, of the Fall of man.

This is a difficult conception, often written off as an incomprehensible or even perverse fantasy nowadays, when the whole emphasis is on the rise of man (though it may perhaps be written off a little less confidently today, after two world wars and their attendant activities, than it was fifty years ago). Naturally, it seems hardly possible to reconcile a 'Fall of man' with the usual picture of his evolutionary ascent. But if we enlarge the picture,[1] we can imagine that the Fall of man was connected with his first appearance as man on earth. Perhaps his premature appearance, from one point of view—but it would be out of place here to go into the background of this always mysterious subject. Two points are relevant. First, the Fall of man is (for me at least) easier to envisage if one sees it not as a once-for-all event, but as a long, slow process. Second, it gives evidence of itself not only in man's moral nature, as a 'fall into sin', but also in his consciousness and ways of thinking.

We may picture it as a gradual journey away from the Source—

[1] See Chapters III and IV.

perhaps decisively initiated, for a journey must have a starting-point—but as a journey that has continued through time. In terms of consciousness it has meant (as already suggested) a loss of participation, a narrowing of the focus, but also the gain of a new capacity for bringing a detached, clear-sighted scrutiny to bear on the outer world, thus making possible (among other things) the rise of modern science. But it seems that the journey has now reached a critical stage: the alienation of consciousness from its source can hardly go much further without finally imprisoning humanity (as it is already tending to do) in a sub-human world, dominated by technology and drained of meaning.

Here I should add that to regard the Fall as a fall into material existence does not imply a so-called Manichean view of matter as inherently 'evil'. Whether this really was the original Manichean view is doubtful; in any case it is not the view I am suggesting. I would regard the material world as a field of action in which certain human capacities could develop only under conditions of progressive severance from the source; somewhat as darkness has impelled men to make their own lamps.

Christianity has been weakened and narrowed, I think, by having emphasized almost exclusively the moral aspect of the Fall, an entirely genuine aspect but not the only one. When the challenge of science came, Christianity could offer no other way of gaining valid knowledge about the world, and when Blake spoke of 'single vision and Newton's sleep', Christian theologians were baffled, or thought him mad. If it had been possible for them to say with authority that the Fall was a fall into illusion as well as into sin, and that the new analytical philosophy would prove to be a way to power rather than truth, the whole realm of reliable knowledge would not have been handed over to science, and the later relations between religion and science would have been very different.[1]

In the New Testament, the Greek word μετανοειτε, usually

---

[1] The Cambridge Platonists in the seventeenth century did try to say something rather like this, but their short-lived endeavours were never followed up.

translated as 'Repent ye', means literally 'Change your mind'. The usual translation can be justified, and even in English 'repentance' used to have (e.g. in Bunyan) a broader sense than it generally has now, implying not simply a contrite abjuration of sin but a radical conversion. But I believe that in the customary interpretation of the Baptist's call something essential is obscured: we should hear in it a summons to a new state of consciousness— 'Change your ways of thinking'—a summons that can be heard again in some of the parables.

Or consider the even more familiar injunction: 'Except ye become as little children . . .' These words have generally been taken to refer to moral innocence; the picture is of a child un- sullied by the world. In spite of the Freudian discoveries, I be- lieve there is some truth in this old picture; the infantile desires and fantasies do not account for the whole being of the child. But the old picture is not entirely true; moreover, to ask an adult to recover the moral innocence of a child seems almost to be asking him to cease to be an adult. The words can also be taken to signify the imaginative, participating consciousness of a child—some- thing that *can* be re-created in an adult mode.

This one-sided emphasis on the moral aspect of the Fall can be explained partly in terms of power: a Church gains influence by offering ways of absolution from sin through its offices, and it will always tend to be suspicious of any claim that an individual can independently raise his consciousness to higher levels of apprehension. Hence the great mystics have seldom received official recognition until some while after they were safely dead. But these tendencies are a reflection also of the autumnal season in the history of consciousness during which Christianity arose.

It was a time of disillusion, scepticism, 'loss of nerve'; little of the old participating consciousness was left. Hence it has been said that during his life on earth Christ was recognized most readily by demons or 'unclean spirits'[1]—i.e. by powers active in the unconscious. During subsequent centuries, while this autumn of consciousness was passing into winter, the Church had to struggle with the chaos and violence that came with the fall of the

[1] Matthew viii, 29; Mark v, 7; Luke iv, 21; viii, 28.

Roman Empire; it was perhaps inevitable that the emphasis should be placed on sin and redemption from sin, and only to be expected that the more esoteric teaching about the Kingdom of God should have been either crudely misinterpreted or entirely obscured.

The Gospels speak, paradoxically, of the Kingdom both as a timeless state of being to be realized inwardly, and as a kingdom that is to 'come'. I think we should not take this 'coming' to signify anything like a reign of Christ on earth. But it suggests that the Christian light was not meant to be a source only of inward illumination or personal redemption, but had a purpose also for the whole creation, manifest and travailing in time.[1]

There is a remarkable contrast in this respect between Christianity and the main Eastern religions (those stemming from Hinduism, Buddhism and Taoism): in them the emphasis is also (I would say) one-sided, in practice if not in doctrine, but in an almost exactly opposite way.

In Eastern religions, too, man is regarded as a fallen being, but the emphasis is on his fall into the darkness of ignorance and the mists of illusion; and his task is to recover knowledge of the truth —not intellectual knowledge, but the direct apprehension that can be gained by inwardly raising himself into the light. Strict standards of morality are enjoined, but observance of them will in itself take a man only a few steps along the path that leads towards enlightenment, release from illusion, and freedom from the wheel of time.

During the not very long period since the Eastern religions first became known in the West, their influence has spread steadily, and perhaps never so rapidly as in the last decade. Many people find in them not only a depth of ancient wisdom absent from orthodox Christianity, but an escape from the sanguinary moral drama of Christian sin and redemption into a wider, serener atmosphere. This can be readily understood, but I think the contrast needs to be brought into relation with the evolution of consciousness.

The Eastern view recognizes what has seldom been recognized in the West: that human consciousness has undergone a narrowing

[1] Romans viii, 22.

and veiling during its journey through time from the Source. But the corresponding gain in objective clarity, and in freedom to explore and analyse the natural world, is something which the Eastern view seems not to recognize, or at any rate not to value at all seriously. One might suppose that this is because the Eastern religions draw their inspiration from an ancient period when the veiling was already apparent and the gain not yet in sight. But a more fundamental reason, perhaps, is that from the Eastern standpoint nothing that happens in time can have ultimate importance, for time itself is part of the shadow-play.

Here is where I would not agree with those who feel that all the great religions are essentially the same. In many of their teachings they are similar, as they must be in so far as the teachings are true, for they belong to the same universe. But Christianity differs from the Eastern religions in its relation to life in time; one might perhaps say that it is the only major religion which takes time seriously.

In the Eastern religions, the Divine remains outside the flux and fever of mortal life; it is viewed rather as the primal source to which men must aspire to return. The essential Christian conception is that the Divine descends into time; enters into the human experience even of death in time. But how could this be a human experience? Perhaps a suggestion comes from the strange words, so often debated and so variously interpreted, 'My God, my God, why hast thou forsaken me?' To me they seem to indicate that Jesus then experienced in full that darkening of consciousness which has been the human lot; experienced indeed the culmination of it which belongs to our own epoch.

Although Christian theology emphasizes the descent of the Divine into time, it does not usually regard as significant the particular time when the incision occurred. Here we can perhaps think by analogy of the sowing of a seed for which the required time is the autumn. At an earlier period it would have been possible for Christ to be recognized in the light of the old consciousness; that is, by a light which had to be lost if the growing down of humanity into material existence was to bear fruit in life and time. And later—the ground would have been too hard.

CHAPTER XXII

Rivers of Time

The evolution of consciousness has been going on for a very long time, and not at all as a straightforward linear process; any short account of it will be misleading. It can be described from many different points of view, all inadequate. One might for instance picture it as a great number of streams of music. They vary widely in tempo, and the tempo of any one of the streams may quicken for a time and then slow down, or come almost to a halt. The streams interweave and are influenced by one another; there are anticipations of later themes and recapitulations with variations of earlier themes. One stream is usually dominant for a time and then another; some streams have never stood out from the background and a few have hardly started to flow.[1]

The early stages have left no tokens: no relics dug up from the earth which will show what it felt like to live at the time when they were new. Later on we can derive indirect evidence from the history of art and language and ways of thinking, and to some extent from the study of such relatively primitive societies as survive today. But it cannot amount to proof; there are no recordings of the lost music of mankind.

No proof—yet on the available evidence it seems strange to suppose that early man experienced his primitive conditions in

---

[1] The vividly emotional Elizabethan period, and the Augustan-classical period of the early eighteenth century, were, I think, recapitulations which overlapped the less evident beginnings of the onlooker-age. Francis Bacon was an untypical but portentous Elizabethan.

160

the same way as we should if we were suddenly transplanted into them. Let us assume that we could forget the amenities of civilization and could feel at ease, crouched round the fire in the draughty cave. For our primitive companions it would still be a different fire, a different cave: a world almost as different from ours as the world of a fish is from the world of a swimmer: in some respects the very opposite of ours.

It was a world devoid of technology but highly charged with *mana*, with psychic potency and meaning: indeed with more meaning, both beneficent and threatening, than early man could cope with; his rituals were largely designed to protect him and his group from it, to step down the current and make it manageable. Our world, rich in technology, has for many people largely lost meaning; such rituals as we retain have the purpose rather of endeavouring to restore contact with a fading current which is widely suspected to have no real existence.

Obviously, the music of mankind has not been all sweet harmony; history is loaded with examples of the hardly credible inhumanity of man to man. They are often attributed to his animal ancestry; but it is not when he is behaving like an animal that he is at his worst. Animals do not act with cold cruelty or calculated ruthlessness or insensate pride. These are distinctive human vices, and not easy to reconcile with the view that the human story is entirely one of evolutionary rise. The view that man has also 'fallen' seems to be more in accord with familiar experience; with the chronic conflict in his nature between his aspirations and his conduct. The more or less insoluble problems relating to the existence of evil and suffering in the world are too wide and deep for an attempted discussion of them here; but they can perhaps be related in certain ways to the evolution of consciousness.

The Genesis story does indeed connect them directly with a change of consciousness. 'Your eyes shall be opened and ye shall be as gods, knowing good and evil.' It sounds rather as though a child were promised that he could be suddenly grown up and enjoy the godlike freedom of adults, but is not warned that if this

L

happens he will have to leave the garden of innocence and go out to earn his living in an unsympathetic world.

I think the Genesis story is describing in its own way a real event—the beginning of human destiny on earth. We need not ask whether this destiny could have been avoided; such a question may be meaningless. The point is that humanity has had the experience of being born on earth out of a condition that might be called pre-natal, and of finding its eyes opening to an external world, together with the corresponding possibility of enjoying private thoughts, a private inner life.[1]

That is one way of speaking about the Fall, a very superficial and incomplete way. The Bible speaks of a war in heaven and of fallen angels: that is, of the establishment in the universe of something resistant to the will of God; without which a material universe as we know it could not have come into being, for to be resistant—to reflect without absorbing—belongs to the essence of the solid matter we know.

Does this mean that but for the Fall there would have been nothing like a material universe? No, that is the heresy of those Gnostics who viewed the material creation as the work of a Demiurge opposed to God. It was (I would say) the will of God that there should be a manifested physical universe, a universe of space and time. The effect of the Fall was to darken and densify the universe, so that to human consciousness matter appears to be hard, resistant, impervious to light.

This applies to the normal consciousness of today, and probably matter has had these characteristics for human consciousness, in some degree, ever since the Fall. The difference is that to the modern consciousness nothing beyond matter is apparent, nothing to suggest a prior condition which matter has fallen from. Many people, nevertheless, are visited by feelings of contrast between the world as it is and the world as it ' ought' to be; or between the world as it is and the aspirations of human beings. In an earlier chapter, also, I mentioned the contrast between the world as it can appear to a slightly heightened consciousness, when it seems to be shot

[1] 'And Adam and his wife hid themselves from the presence of the Lord God.'

through with radiance and wisdom, and the world as it looks to a depressed consciousness, when it appears to be aridly mechanical and meaningless.[1] Here we have intimations, perhaps, of how the Fall has affected the manifested universe, and of what its eventual effects might be if no redemptive action were available.

Hence we ought to think of the material world, not in the Gnostic way as an environment which is opposed to the Divine plan and should therefore be escaped from, but as a darkened version of the original creation, awaiting redemption by the 'sons of God'. The original creation is still there, behind the veil of appearance, and can be apprehended; but merely to apprehend it is not enough. For through the experience of darkening and alienation, possibilities are open to man which would not have been open to him if the Fall had not occurred. Thus he should value the material world both for the ways in which it does reveal the original creation, and as a place in which he has been given exacting responsibilities, for good or ill. He has a responsibility, especially, for the future of the earth and for the conditions of life upon it; for whether the redemptive action initiated by the coming of Christ shall proceed towards something we may call resurrection, or whether earth existence shall go its own way, a kingdom of the fallen, severed (though not everlastingly) from its Source.

Hence we may think of the aftermath of the Fall as a permitted venture; a venture involving very high stakes and bound up with all that we recognize in history as height and depth, heroism and depravity, the unceasing struggle of man divided against himself. The war in heaven continues on earth.

Man has been brought into the midst of this battleground; the conflict goes on within him and without. In conventional mythology it is pictured as a struggle between an angel and a devil, the angel trying to draw the man's soul upwards and the devil trying to drag it down. But this picture is untrue to the human situation. If the virtues are abstracted from human nature and assigned to the angel, they become unreal; for there are few virtues that cannot be abused and few vices in which a distorted image of virtue

[1] Chapter V.

cannot be recognized.[1] To go with the conventional angel would mean renouncing the passionate energies which are as necessary for virtue as for vice.

The real battle for the human soul is between two fallen angels, Lucifer and another. The establishment in the universe of a resistance to the will of God leads to the setting up of two kingdoms; first a kingdom of pride, a pseudo-heaven in which the prevailing doctrine is that the earth is a crude and unnecessary creation which need not be endured by man. This pseudo-heaven was the state of consciousness offered to Eve, and in various forms it is still offered. But it has its counterpart, its 'shadow', in a kingdom which is—or could become—a kind of pseudo-earth; here the principle of resistance hardens into clever self-sufficiency and the prevailing doctrine is that God does not exist. The rulerships of the two kingdoms express the two forms of egotism —the vainglorious and the calculating, the hot and the cold.

It is to these two temptations that man is constantly exposed; and yet, paradoxically, he needs them. Without the one, he would lack the fire of imagination; without the other, the precision of intellect. By resisting them he uses them; the human situation is this battle—the redemption of the contraries, as Blake said.[2]

Something like this has always been the human situation since the birth of man on earth; but the emphasis has changed with evolutionary time. In the early stages the temptation of Lucifer was the stronger, for it played on memories of paradise. In other

[1] Thus of the four cardinal virtues, justice can be coldly rigid; prudence can be pusillanimous; temperance is not the right mood for all occasions; even fortitude can shade into obstinacy.

[2] There are indications of these contrasting but subtly interwoven temptations in the account of the temptation of Jesus in the wilderness. In the Gospels they are of course addressed not to man but to the Son of God; but similar temptations do come, on a different level, to human beings in their wilderness; and modern science has given them added force. The 'stones into bread' temptation is the temptation to suppose that technology can satisfy all human needs. The tempting vision of 'all the kingdoms of the earth and the glory thereof' is familiar enough; it generally carries the suggestion that these are the only kingdoms. The 'pinnacle of the temple' temptation invites us to imagine that men can become 'men like gods', supermen, and that there are in the universe no powers which human ambition cannot safely harness for its own ends.

words, man still had a state of consciousness for which the earth was somewhat foreign; the temptation was to turn away from it as an illusion and not to learn to read its book. But it is in human destiny that the other tempter should have always been present, fulfilling indeed an essential function by holding man to the generations of earthly life; and in our epoch his influence has become the stronger of the two. In other words, human consciousness has evolved to a stage in which the earth has become the solid unquestionable reality, and paradise an ancient myth, remembered only through the dream-symbols of the unconscious mind.

It is thus also possible to picture the evolution of consciousness as a journey through time, but not as a journey in which human figures are seen against an independent landscape setting, subject only to such changes as are recorded in the geological and climatic history of the earth. We must picture rather a continuous transformation-scene, with the human figures at first hardly distinguishable from the background. This is the early stage in which man does not yet experience himself as having an independent existence over against nature, but as part of a nature which both sustains and threatens him.

As time goes on, the human figures become more distinct; they begin to work on nature, not only magically, but with hoe and plough. Later still, the human figures are questioning nature and at the same time asking questions about themselves. The scale of the picture changes; the stars are now far off. The human figures feel they are living in a vast universe which gives them no evidence of the Divine, except through an intellectual 'argument from design', and that has doubtful implications and is losing force.

This is a verdict that belongs to the onlooker-consciousness of our epoch; it is not therefore conclusive. But a true verdict is not to be looked for from a revival of the old 'magical feeling'. That *would* lead to fantasies, for it reflects a relationship of man to the world which is not only no longer valid, but actually unattainable—as unattainable as lost youth. For it is not only man's relationship to nature which has changed, but the relationship of nature to the Divine powers which sustain it—as they always do and must, but now at a certain remove:

O air scarce-stirred with the Court's far junketing . . .[1]

Hence the onlooker-consciousness, while subject to illusion in supposing that the worlds known to science and the senses are all there is, reflects a certain truth when it sees in the heavens the 'army of unalterable law'; when it is impressed by the enormous empty spaces and distances of the cosmos; or when it suggests that if a Deity exists, he must be a mathematician.

But the onlooker-consciousness is not a final stage. It is an extreme condition, and a critical one, for if it were to continue unillumined, it could lead on to the imprisonment of humanity in the only world it knows; and not only the world of technology that *we* know, but a development of it into the pseudo-earth which is the goal of the second temptation.

The constant aim of this temptation has always been to conceal from man an awareness of his spiritual origin; to persuade him that the earth is his only home; and to keep him there in the ultimate guise of something like a mechanized intelligence, cut off from the Source.

The onlooker-consciousness brings about also a critical stage in personal relationships. Here again, it seems to me, Mr. Wren-Lewis and those who think with him are in a sense right. They are right in reminding us that Christianity calls for two or three being gathered together, and right in feeling that in our epoch it is becoming possible—though far from easy—for persons to meet persons in a new way.

In earlier periods, people mostly wore uniforms—protective garments marking their caste or function or social rank. Those were the times when everyone 'knew his place'. Today, nobody quite knows his place, for there are, in theory, no places to know. In many societies, and notably in our own, strong class distinctions persist, but they are no longer accepted as belonging to the natural order of things.

[1] From *Maerchen*, by Walter de la Mare.

This new situation occurs partly though social-economic changes, but also because for the onlooker-consciousness the uniforms no longer carry their old 'magical' aura. Thus in our epoch people are gradually compelled more and more to meet nakedly, face to face—or with only the uncertain protection of the individual mask, the persona, which in some degree is worn by everyone.

It is not surprising that new strains and tensions develop: married life, for instance, was in many respects much easier when husband and wife each had and accepted a clearly assigned role in the partnership. For them to meet as equal, independent persons is far more exacting, but can be much more rewarding.

Something similar results from the fact that the onlooker-consciousness tends by its own nature towards coldness and objectivity. One might assume that this is obviously bad for personal relationships, but it can offer release from the smothering, possessive kind of affection in which a great deal of egoism is usually concealed. It *can*—but it can also lead to a manipulative use of other persons as things. That is the critical question: the question of love in the cold climate of the onlooker-age.

I believe that in this apparently unpromising climate it is possible for personal relationships to be more truly personal than they generally were in the past, but only where the onlooker-consciousness takes the right turning at its crossroads, so to speak. It takes the wrong turning if—often under the influence of the conventional scientific picture of man—it tends to treat persons as tools or units or things, as it very easily can. It takes the right turning if, proceeding from objectivity, it develops the insight which can recognize a human spirit behind the other's perhaps tormented or even hostile mask.

There is no way of describing this recognition to anyone who finds it incomprehensible or meaningless. It leads to an I-Thou relationship, as distinct from I-It, in Martin Buber's famous phrase. It implies also acceptance, the forgiveness that we all need from one another. It is not incompatible with sexual love; though passionate love may make it harder to maintain. It is a religious recognition, but may arise between persons with no

167

definite religious beliefs; in that case it creates a kind of religion, which may be unrecognized and transient, between them. It can occur within the framework of any religion, but I believe it has a particular connection with Christiantiy, for the injunctions of Christ were directed against those limiting ties of race and caste and family and sex which had governed most personal relationships until then, and still do so widely.

If in the future we approach anything resembling a Christian society, it will be marked, I think, by ways of living in which relations between persons will be very much closer and yet less binding, more varied in forms of affection and sympathy, but less dependent on background and circumstances, than they are to-day. There will be freedom in community, and the acceptance of angularities and uncongenial opinions in others will not go only as far as some convention of tolerance requires.[1]

In such a society, if we can dimly envisage it, it may be possible to clear away some of the confusion which surrounds the ideas of 'ego' and 'egoism'. Egoism is bound up with emotional and bodily cravings and desires; the ego which identifies itself with this perpetual surge is different from what I think of as the human spirit, which by its own nature is as ready to give as to receive. By purgation, the centre of consciousness can become more representative of the spirit and less of the ego, but the spirit never comes to complete expression in earthly life.

Evolution has led to enhanced selfconsciousness and so to heightened egoism; the earth-bound ego, feeling itself alone and in relative freedom, is impelled to assert itself. This I would not regard as a mere aberration, but as something like the painful process of emerging into awkward adolescence. Here, again, the onlooker-epoch marks a critical stage: it offers opportunities both for more deliberate egoism and for developing that detachment from oneself in which egoism is partially overcome. This is a slow and difficult process, constantly defeated, but more relevant to the tasks of human living than any attempt to have done with

[1] I am not suggesting that a society could be Christian throughout, only that in it such ways of living might not be rare.

egoism by merging oneself in a mystical 'all'. Such attempts lead readily to illusions; they are the opposite of the more familiar illusion whereby the earth-bound ego, with its accretion of conflicting desires, is itself expected to inherit eternity.

There are good grounds for believing that the essential human spirit, not being wholly subject to life, is not subject to death; but here too it may be easy to fall into errors of a rather different kind. To me it seems probable that in its own realm the spirit may not wholly possess itself, but exists in indispensable relation to other spirits; a relation that stretches back far beyond one earthly life. It is this interdependence of human spirits, in time and out of time, which would perhaps be imaged faintly in what I have thought of as a future Christian society on earth. The other would not be wholly other, any more than myself would be wholly mine.

The recognition of the human spirit in a person calls for an imaginative insight not essentially different, I believe, from the imagination which is required for the Goethean-artistic approach to nature and the rest of the outer world. To say confidently that there is nothing 'behind' nature, no 'meaning' to be discerned there, is to me rather like saying that behind a human face there is nothing but flesh and bone. Hence it seems strange to propose that religion and 'transcendence' should be confined to the experience of personal relationships, while the outer world remains meaningless. The suggestion is that the experience of love between persons will provide the inspiration and the standard for transforming the world, with the aid of science, into a world fit for persons, but it seems at least equally likely that a world apprehended as meaningless, where no trace of transcendence could be found, would impose its own chilling shadow on personal relationships.

This is indeed what one might expect in the light of history, for changes in personal relationships and in the relation of man to nature have followed a parallel course. In early epochs man was not free to stand apart and decide what he would think or feel about nature, any more than he was free to decide with whom he would have close personal associations. Nature poured 'meaning' into him in abundance; and his personal relations were subject to tribal traditions and kinship rules. The evolution of consciousness has now at last brought him to a stage in which he is detached and free: free to treat nature more or less as he chooses, and free to form whatever personal relations or social systems he fancies. In both fields he can choose between 'I-Thou' and 'I-It' relationships; and in both he is equipped with unprecedented powers for exploitation and enslavement, if that is his choice.[1]

How familiar, painfully familiar, these words sound! The phraseology may be a trifle odd, but are we not told every other day, in newspapers and speeches and sermons, much the same thing? The human race has got hold of powers far in excess of its capacity to control them, far in excess of its moral stature: there is a great danger that they will be used for the destruction of the world. But we hear also that this is a pre-eminently hopeful time, hazardous no doubt but full of promise—for science has at last driven away the fogs of superstition and the human race is free to set about making a world in which most of the scourges of mankind will eventually be overcome—free indeed to break through earthbound limitations and become the explorers of outer space.

The conflicting voices of the two cultures can be heard here, and both can claim on strong grounds to be justified. My aim has not been to argue one against the other, but to discuss their conflict and its origin in the light of the evolution of consciousness, believing that this neglected historical light can help powerfully to illuminate the human situation today.

There are signs that the idea of the evolution of consciousness is coming to be—not accepted, but regarded here and there as not wholly fantastic; an idea that should perhaps be cautiously reckoned with. To me it is not simply a more or less plausible

---

[1] An 'I-Thou' approach to nature does not imply sentimentality; a sentimental approach is in fact a mild form of exploitation, well-meaning perhaps but none the less degrading. The point is to seek to understand the processes of nature and to work in co-operation with them. This is a quite practical and scientific approach—far more so in the long run than greedy exploitation.

theory, but something that can be experienced, up to a point, in oneself. It is not difficult at any rate to reach the experience that the possibilities of consciousness are manifold, and to become aware of the special characteristics of the bright, clear, limited consciousness of the present day. But I realize very well that for many people the idea will remain profoundly uncongenial, for diverse reasons. To most scientists it will appear nebulous, un-provable, unnecessary, and—much worse—irredeemably tinged with 'magical feeling'. Anyone who finds the existing scientific picture of the world entirely satisfying will have no use for the evolution of consciousness; although he may seem to me to illus-trate it rather clearly.

To many religious people the idea will remain uncongenial on quite different grounds. They will feel that to discuss it in the way I have done is to invade the mysteries of religion and to secularize them; to make them subject to history and to time. One should not try to explain in conceptual terms any things of this kind: they are approachable only through parables. In par-ticular, to speak of an evolutionary process as having in some way changed the relation of man to God is almost blasphemous.

I would agree that the mysteries of religion are best approached through parables—but what is a parable? 'A man's life of any worth is a continual allegory,' Keats wrote.[1] My aim has been to consider human history as a parable throughout, a book of revelation which one must try haltingly to read. That is the true element in 'magical feeling'. The alternative is to regard human history as accidental and meaningless—hardly a religious ap-proach.

The objection that a process in time cannot affect the relation of man to God ought not to come from Christians; but Christian theologians have generally recognized only a single incursion of the Divine into time, and they have had great difficulty in finding any room in the world's history for the Fall, although its pro-found influence on the situation of man, and on his need for redemption, is an essential part of Christian doctrine. In relation to the evolution of consciousness the Fall appears as a continuing

[1] Letter to George and Georgiana Keats, February–May 1819.

influence, not contained in time but spreading through time, which need not be taken on faith but can be experienced and *partially* understood. Yet it should be said (if it needs saying) that the alienation of man from God which the Fall brings about is never complete.[1] In no epoch is the dimension of transcendence, which cuts as it were vertically into the stream of time, ever closed; nor is the Grace to approach it withheld. But a father sends his children out into the world; their communication with him will not then be the same as it was in childhood; it cannot be as easy and direct. By working in the world they will gain experience which severs them from childhood; but when they return from their far country, the father's door will not be closed.

The objection to reading so much into a temporal process would come more naturally from the standpoint of Eastern religions. From their Himalaya the course of human history looks fairly uniform: the mass of people have always lived in a realm of illusion and a few have always pierced through it and found release. Here one should perhaps recognize that the Eastern religions are illumined by the wisdom of a distant past; a high wisdom still bearing the character of an early stage in the human journey, when life on earth in time was experienced somewhat as a dream, and when effort was needed, not to discern the powers of the spirit, but to see the outer world clearly and to take seriously its responsibilities.

Up to now the influence of the onlooker-consciousness has been most marked in the West. Probably it will spread round the world, with the advance of science and technology. It is a winter consciousness. This is another way in which the long history of man can be pictured—through the seasons. In this picture, summer comes first: the time when nature is abundant and men in their activities and their feelings go out into nature. It is in summer that we today can most readily gain some inkling of what it was like to live in epochs when man and nature were at one.

Evolution proceeded to autumn; the skies of consciousness darkened and men turned their thoughts to earth. We are now in

[1] Romans viii, 38–9.

winter; the days are short and the stars on clear nights are remote. But the earth has been so transformed that the change is not very noticeable; we keep our cities warm and bright. We have come far from the dreamy moods of summer; our thinking is as clear and sharp as frost.

It is quite possible to continue living in winter; technology will turn stones into bread. But we ought to understand our situation; how we have reached it and what can be made of it. The winter experience has been indispensable; but the imagination of man has power to quicken the dry earth and bring in a new season.

Index

Abolition of Man, The, 103
Adams, George, 131 n.
Adaptive radiation, 33
Agriculture, 81 sqq.
Albertus, Magnus, 79 n.
Alchemy, 63 n., 65, 76 sqq., 81
An Adventure, 25 n.
Animals without Backbones, 35 n.
Anselm, St., 54
Aquinas, St. Thomas, 55–7
Aristotle, 52–5
Art and the Creative Unconscious, 49 n.
Arts Council, 136
Ashmole, Elias, 77 n.
Asimov, I., 146 n.
Atwood, Mary Anne, 80 n.
Auden, W. H., 65 n.
Australian aborigines, 49

Backhouse, William, 77 n.
Bacon, Francis, 65, 160 n.
Baptist, John the, 157
Barfield, Owen, 50 n., 72, 97 n.
Battle for the Mind, 85 n.
Bees, 83 n.
Bertalanffy, L. von, 124–5
Biographia Literaria, Coleridge's, 73
Blake, William, 65 sqq., 71–3, 99 n., 154, 156, 164
Branfield, Wilfred, 42 n.
Bronowski, J., 66 n., 91 n.
Buber, Martin, 167
Buddhism, 158
Bunyan, John, 157

Cambridge Platonists, 156 n.
Carter, G. S., 35 n., 36 n.
Celtic Christianity, 25 n.
Chalk formations, 42
Chartres, School of, 55
Chasles, Michel, 132 n.
Child and Man, 67 n.
Christian Fathers, 25
Christianity, coming of, 52–3, 159
Cicero and the Roman Republic, 53 n.
Clairvoyance, 115
Clark, James M., 59 n.
Coleridge, 66–7, 70, 72–3
Colour, Goethe's and Newton's Theories of, 68–9
Common Sense of Science, 91 n.
Communism, 11, 15, 142–3, 145
Constantine, 53
Continuous Creation, 42 n.
Cosmology, 20
Counter-current, 88, 89, 94, 104, 145
Crookall, Dr. Robert, 112 n.
Crottet, Robert, 22
Cubism, 135 n.

Dance of Death, 59 n.
Darwin, Charles, 64 n., 65 n.
Darwinism, 30 sqq., 36–9
Darwin's Finches, 33 n.
De la Mare, Walter, 166 n.
Decline and Fall, 80 n.
Descartes, 140
Dickens, Charles, 134
Dieppe Raid case, 25 n.

'Dissociation of sensibility', 63–4
Donne, 63, 64
Doors of Perception, The, 44 n.
'Doubting Thomas', 60
Dowsing, 27
Dreamtime, The (Alcheringa), 49
Dryads, 52
Dryden, 63
Duns Scotus, 55

Eleven-plus, 152
Eliot, T. S., 63, 64, 97 n.
Encounter, 11
England in the Eighteenth Century, 71 n.
English Philosophy since 1900, 74 n.
Equality, 144–5
'Escape from Specialisation', 37 n.
Evolution and the Image of Man, 36 n.
Evolution as a Process, 32 n., 35 n., 37 n.
Evolution of language, 50

Faithful Thinker, The, 36 n., 131 n.
Fall of Man, Chap. xxi,162 sqq., 171
Farbenlehre, 68
Fascism, 142
Fausset, Hugh I'A., 117 n.
Fawcett, Douglas, 41 n.
Feeling and Form, 135 n.
Feiling, Keith, 71 n.
Fisher, R. A., 23, 32, 34, 36
Fordham, Frieda, 108 n.
Forster, E. M., 146 n.
Fraternity, 143–5
Freud, 97–8

G.C.E., 152
Geddes, Auckland, 112 n.
Genesis, Book of, 161–2
Genetic drift, 34
Genetical recombination, 33
Geometry, projective, Chap. xvii
Gibbon, 80 n.
Gnostics, 162–3
Goethe, 68–9, 119, 121–7, 128, 132–3

Goethe's Conception of the World, 69 n.
Goethe the Alchemist, 78 n.
Goethean Science Foundation, 131 n.
Golden Age, 51
Gordon Davis case, 26 n.
Gray, R. D., 78 n.
Gray, Sir James, 84 n.
Greeks, The, 51–2
Growing up, Chap. xx

Haldane, J. B. S., 34
Hardy, A. C., 37 n.
Harwood, A. C., 67 n., 147 n., 151 n.
Hawkes, Jacquetta, 97 n., 139 n.
Hermetic philosophy, 80, 80 n.
Hesse, Mary, 90 n.
Heywood, Rosalind, 44 n.
Hierarchies, 126
Hinduism, 158
History in English Words, 50 n.
Homoeopathy, 22 n.
Hoyle, Fred, 109 n.
Huizinga, J., 59 n.
Humpty Dumpty, 87
Hundred Years of Evolution, A, 35 n.
Huxley, Aldous, 44 n., 141 n.
Huxley, Julian, 32
Hyams, Edward, 82 n.
Hypnosis, 25, 26–7

Idea of Progress, The, 52 n.
Ideas of Good and Evil, 62 n.
Imagists, 135
Industrialism, beginnings of modern, 61, 71, 134
Initiation, 107–8, 122 n.
Introduction to Jung's Psychology, An, 108 n.
Invisible Writing, The, 23 n.
IQ, 151, 152
Ivy, Sister, 46

Jacks, G. V. and Whyte, R. O., 82 n
Jaspers, Karl, 122 n.

Jenks, Jorian, 82 n.
Johnson, Raynor C., 41 n., 46 n.
Jowett, Dr., 28
Jung, 62, 97 n., 108 n., 117 n.

Keats, John, 171
Kermode, Professor Frank, 64
Kingdom of God, 99 n., 158
Knowledge of Higher Worlds, 117 n.
Koestler, Arthur, 23

Langer, Suzanne K., 135 n.
Lawrence, D. H., 62, 111, 140, 142, 154
Lehrs, Ernst, 69 n., 121 n.
Lewis, C. S., 103
Life and Letters of Charles Darwin, 65 n.
Life of St. Thomas Aquinas, The 56 n.
Linnell, 66 n.
Listener, The, 22 n., 95 n.
Locher-Ernst, L., 131 n.
Locke, William, 65
Logical Positivism, 74
Lonely Crowd, The, 145 n.
'Loss of Nerve', 157
Lucifer, 164
Lysergic acid, 44

Machine Stops, The, 146 n.
'Magical Feeling', 94 sqq.
Man on Earth, 139 n.
Man or Matter, 69 n., 121 n.
Man Without a Mask, A., 66 n.
Manchester Guardian, 44 n.
Manichean, 156
Mark, The, 117 n.
Marx, Karl, 143
Maya, 41
Mediumship, 25–6
Mescalin, 44, 45
Metaphysical Poets, The, 63
Meteorologists, 114
Milton, 63, 64
Modern Science and Modern Man, 28 n.
Muller, H. J., 34

Mumford, Lewis, 59 n.
Mysteries, ancient, 107, 110
Mystical Life, The, 112 n.
Mysticism, Sacred and Profane, 46 n.

Naked Sun, The, 146 n.
Natural Selection, 30 sqq.
Neumann, Erich, 49 n.
'New imagination', 115
New Jerusalem, 81 n.
New Statesman, 18
New Year Letter, 65 n.
Newton, Isaac, 63, 65, 68–9, 106
Nicoll, Maurice, 117 n.
Nominalism, 53, 54–7, 58, 74
Nurslings of Immortality, 41 n.

Observer, The, 82 n.
Occam, William of, 56–7
Organization Man, The, 145 n.
Origin of Species, 38
Osborn, Fairfield, 82 n.

Philosopher's Stone, 77, 78 n.
Plato, 52, 54–5
Plumb, J. H., 71 n.
Pneuma, 50, 77
Poetic Diction, 50 n.
Prelude to Chemistry, 79 n.
Priestley, J. B., 97 n.
Principia, 63
Problems of Life, 124 n.
Projection, 49, 97, 116
Protestants, early, 60
Puberty, 152–3

Radiesthesia, 25, 27
Raine, Kathleen, 97 n.
Rape of the Earth, 82 n.
Read, John, 79 n.
Rede Lecture (C. P. Snow), 11 sqq.
Reichenbach, Hans, 23
Rhine, J. B. ,23
Riesman, David, 145 n.
Rise of the Meritocracy, The, 144 n.
Roberts, Michael, 82 n.
Roman Empire, 158

Romans, the, 53
Romantic Image, 64 n.
Romantic Revival (and Movement), 65 sqq., 71–5, 115, 134
Romanticism Comes of Age, 72 n.

Sargant, William, 85 n.
Saving the Appearances, 50 n.
Science and the Human Imagination, 90 n.
Semita Recta, 79 n.
Shakespeare, 67 n.
Sister Ivy, 46
Skolt Lapps, 22
Snow, C. P., 11, 12, 14, 15, 17, 21
Society for Psychical Research, 25 n., 26 n.
Soil and Civilisation, 82 n.
Space, anti-Euclidean, 130–2
Starkey, G., 78 n.
Steiner, Rudolf, 43, 69 n., 97 n., 117 n., 126, 131 n., 132 n., 137 n., 148 n.
Study and Practice of Astral Projection, The, 112 n.
Suggestive Inquiry into the Hermetic Mystery, 80 n.
Surrealism, 135
Symbolic, 48, 50
Symbolists, etc., 104–5
Synod of Whitby, 25 n.

Taoism, 158
Taylor, Dr. F. Sherwood, 45, 78 n., 79 n.
Technics and Civilisation, 59 n.
Telepathy, 22, 25–6
Temptations in the Wilderness, 164 n.

Third Culture, 90, 93, 110, 115
Three Spheres of Society, The, 143 n.
Threshold, crossing the, 108, 117
Times, The, 83 n.
Transcendence, 172
Truth and Symbol, 122 n.
Twentieth Century, The, 95 n., 100 n.

Undiscovered Self, The, 117 n.
Uniforms, 166–7
Urpflanze, 122–3

Virtues, cardinal, 164 n.
Von Seelen rätseln, 137 n.
Vorticism, 135

Waning of the Middle Ages, The, 59 n.
War in heaven, 162
Warnock, G. J., 74 n.
Waterman, Charles, 143 n.
Waterman, John, 36 n.
Wegman, Ita, 132 n.
Whicher, Olive, 131 n.
Whiteman, Dr. J. H. M., 112 n.
Whyte, W. H., 145 n.
Will, acts of, 137
Wren-Lewis, John, 94 sqq., 106 n., 166
Wright, Sewall, 34

Yeats, W. B., 62 n.
Young, Michael, 144 n.

Zaehner, R. C., 46 n.
Zermatt Dialogues, 41 n.